Generation SICK

Generation SICK

The Power, Politics and Propaganda Behind America's Health Crisis

Dr. Vic Naumov

Cover: Chris Martillo Design

ISBN-10: 0996960406
ISBN-13: 9780996960403
Library of Congress Control Number: 2015919251
Victor Naumov, New Milford, NJ

Vincent Crow Press, P.O. Box 206, New Milford, NJ 07646

Dedication

To my beautiful wife of over 20 years, Colleen, and to my two amazing sons Bryant and Conor. This book is my gift to you. May you never forget, "Your health is your wealth. Guard it well." I love the three of you with all my heart and more than any words can ever express. "Remember to always love more than your heart can hold, laugh more than your lungs can breathe and live more than your mind can dream."

To the citizens of the United States of America: Because it's always better to light a candle than to curse the darkness.

Finally...To the beloved memory of my grandparents, Fedor and Maria Naumov. You will always be my cornerstone.

Disclaimer

C onsult a medical doctor or other licensed medical professional if you suffer from any medical conditions. This publication presents only the author's opinions, which are based on his knowledge, experiences and beliefs. This book and its contents do not cure, prevent, diagnose or treat any disease or condition. The purpose for this book is educational, research and entertainment. The information contained within this book is for informational purposes only. The author, the publisher and everybody involved with the publication, distribution or sale of this book assume no responsibility.

Contents

Acknowledgments

"I think apologizing is a great thing, but you have to be wrong."
— DONALD TRUMP

Writing a book is a lonely endeavor, like a solo flight across the Atlantic, an attempt to break the Guinness Book full-body ice contact endurance record or a 12-hour rehearsal in the practice room two months before a Wigmore Hall debut. This book, whatever its limitations, was five years in the making and represents a lifetime of thought on health and nutrition issues, subjects that are of the utmost importance to me and (I humbly submit) to the future of our country. I tip my hat to any reader who is able to make it through the book and finds some of my opinions useful and salutary.

Thank you to Patrick Clark, my editor, who guided my musings, sharpened and polished my expressions and helped insure that the book would be readable and relevant to people outside my usual circles. Patrick proved more than equal to the task. I could not be more proud of the finished product. I am grateful to my good friend Richard Cassaro, author of *Written in Stone*, for sharing his secret weapon with me.

I would also like to thank Chris Martillo of *Chris Martillo Design* for creating such an amazing cover for this book. You are the hidden gem in the graphic art world. Your vision, together with my ideas, created a killer cover. You rock, brother! I'm so glad to call you a dear friend and a member of my team.

My reading has included, besides the standard works on health and nutrition, more than a few books by people whom mainstream scholars regard as wrong-headed and dangerous cranks, curmudgeons, conspiracy theorists, and proponents of viewpoints that history has ignored or demoted. I make no apologies for my choice of reading matter, nor should you. I stand by every line in this book, even though I acknowledge that future editions will probably include caveats, clarifications or even minor contradictions to certain of the viewpoints expressed herein. Live and learn, there's nothing wrong with that.

My chiropractic practice members and the clients of my nutrition advisory business have taught me more than anyone has a right to know about the consequences of making sound health decisions under difficult circumstances. I have gained the courage to state my thoughts without fear of potential adverse consequences from practice members who bravely faced agonizing decisions about their health. Many of them shared with me their experiences with the healthcare system; and some of the rage you may detect in the book springs in part from disturbing, even painful, conversations with practice members about the criminal negligence and mistreatment they suffered at the hands of a healthcare system that is based on principles other than strictly humane ones.

I want to thank my late grandparents, Fedor and Maria Naumov, for loving me for who I am and respecting me for my life's journey.

More than anyone else, my beloved wife, Colleen Naumov, has been the inspiration and sounding board for my best ideas. Without her generous support and sound advice, I would probably never have committed the first word of this book to paper. I also want to thank our two amazing sons, Bryant and Conor, who give me firm grounds for hope that the next generation will be a little less sick than this one.

Forward

"I am not here to change the world. I am here to change myself and to protect my children at all costs, so that they have the right to grow and live longer and better than I do. All in accordance with Natural Law."

— VINCENT CROW

THEY claim that, *"Health is Wealth."* If that is a fact, shouldn't the wealthiest country in the world be the healthiest? The United States of America generates, per capita, the most wealth in the world. So, then I ask you, why does it rank dead last when it comes to health out of a list of the top 11 countries in the world?

After Dr. Vic Naumov asked me to write the *Forward* for *Generation SICK*, I began my research and came across an interesting article published June 16, 2014 authored by Mary Mahon and Bethanne Fox. The title reads: *"U.S. Health System Ranks Last Among Eleven Countries on Measures of Access, Equality, Quality, Efficiency and Healthy Lives."*

Wow...was I surprised because I (like you) was conditioned to believe that the United States of America, was the wealthiest country and had the greatest healthcare system in the world. I guess I was seriously misled because the following data collected proves otherwise. Since the United States also has the most expensive healthcare system in the world, I accepted the understanding that the most expensive automatically meant *"the best."* What I learned was this was absolutely not the case. Not by a long shot. The list of countries included in the study were Australia, Canada, France, Germany, the Netherlands, New Zealand, Norway, Sweden, Switzerland and the United Kingdom.

Key findings related to the United States of America within this report include:

Healthy lives: The U.S. does poorly, ranking last on infant mortality and on deaths that were potentially preventable with timely access to effective health care and second-to-last on healthy life expectancy at age 60.

Access to care: People in the U.S. have the hardest time affording the healthcare they need. The U.S. ranks last on every measure of cost-related access. More than one-third (37%) of U.S. adults reported forgoing a recommended test, treatment or follow-up care because of cost.

Health care quality: The U.S ranks in the middle. On two of four measures of quality—effective care and patient-centered care—the U.S. ranks near the top (3rd and 4th of 11 countries, respectively), but it does not perform as well providing safe or coordinated care.

Efficiency: The U.S ranks last, due to low marks on the time and dollars spent dealing with insurance administration, lack of communication among health care providers and duplicative medical testing. Forty percent of U.S. adults who had visited an emergency room reported they could have been treated by a regular doctor, had one been available. This is more than double the rate of patients in the U.K. (16%).

Equity: The U.S. ranks last. About four of 10 (39%) adults with below-average incomes in the U.S. reported a medical problem but did not visit a doctor in the past year because of costs, compared with less than one of 10 in the U.K., Sweden, Canada, and Norway. There were also large discrepancies between the length of time U.S. adults waited for specialist, emergency and after-hours care compared with higher-income adults.

The fact that the United States ranked *"dead last"* in the above categories seriously concerns me. It concerns me not only for myself, but also for my family, my community and my country. *"We as Americans deserve to be healthy!"*

Before we quickly begin to act on emotion, a step back is necessary. It is only when we understand the "Cause and Effect" principle, that we can begin to clearly see that we didn't get here by accident. I would speculate that we got here by design. In business and politics, nothing happens by accident. Everything in the public domain happens by design regardless of what things look like on the surface. Healthcare is big business in the United States and as you can see, it is also the most expensive in the world. However, even with all that money injected into the system, the results fall short of expectations. As a result, people are getting sicker and sicker while their pain and suffering continues to fund a system that seems to be a failure since its inception in 1913 by John D. Rockefeller, Sr.

I've always wanted to know "Why" the richest country in the world had one of the least successful healthcare systems. As I continued to search for answers, my research uncovered an interesting book by Eustace Mullins titled "*Murder By Injection.*" This book gave me the documented answers I was looking for. I finally began to understand that the allopathic medical system was set up by John D. Rockefeller, Sr., not to help, heal or cure any diseases, but rather to create profit through life-long customers driven by pain, suffering and the continued consumption of poisonous drugs.

On page 348 (the last page) Mullins wrote, "*America became the greatest and most productive nation in the world because we had the healthiest citizens in the world. When the Rockefeller Syndicate began its takeover of our medical profession in 1910, our citizens went into a sharp decline. Today, we suffer from a host of debilitating ailments, both mental and physical, nearly all of which can be traced directly to the operations of the chemical and drug monopoly, and which poses the greatest threat to our continued existence as a nation. Unite now to restore our national health--the result will be the restoration of our national pride, the resumption of our role as inventors and producers of the modern world, and the custodian of the world's hopes and dreams of the liberty of freedom.*" These are powerful words, from a brilliant man who understood that "*Heath IS Wealth.*"

As a result of John D. Rockefeller's efforts, today, we are still sick, still tired and dead last in healthcare out of the top 11 countries. For the sake of the American people and future generations, it should not be this way. In my opinion, it is a disgrace and a testament to the failure of both the allopathic healthcare system and the hidden hand of the Rockefeller Foundation that controls it. Education, awareness and action are the three essentials necessary to facilitate any type of change if our goal as a society is to be truly healthy. The next generation depends upon us.

What type of legacy do we want to leave for our children? Do we really want to raise another *Generation SICK*? I sure don't. What are we going to do today, to bring about the change we want to see tomorrow? It is important to understand, "*Knowing and not doing means you don't know anything at all.*"

Our children deserve better. Let me correct myself. Our children deserve the best we have to offer. They are our future and deserve the opportunity to live their lives to their fullest potential.

Dr. Vic Naumov wrote this informative, explosive book so that you will finally learn the facts behind...how we got here, who gave us our current allopathic medical system, who controls it and what the ultimate agenda is. After reading this book, ignorance is no longer an excuse and sickness does not have to be looked upon as a normal way of life.

This book is the game changer you have been looking for and holds within it the potential to *"restore the power to the people."* The time to rise, get informed and take action is now! We ALL deserve the opportunity to be HEALTHY!

Yours in Health,

Vincent Crow
Advocate for Healthcare Freedom, Liberty and Individual Prosperity

Introduction

"World events do not occur by accident. They are made to happen, whether it is to do with national issues or commerce; and most of them are staged and managed by those who hold the purse strings."

— Dennis Healy, UK Secretary of State for Defense from 1964 to 1970 and Chancellor of the Exchequer from 1974 to 1979

"Unless we put medical freedom into the Constitution, the time will come when medicine will organize an undercover dictatorship. To restrict the art of healing to one class of men, and deny equal privilege to others, will be to constitute the Bastille of medical science. All such laws are un-American and despotic, and have no place in a Republic. The Constitution of this Republic should make special privilege for medical freedom as well as religious freedom."

— Benjamin Rush, MD
Signer of the Declaration of Independence

As I look at the current state of affairs within the United States of America and the rest of the world, I constantly find myself thinking that "nothing is what it appears to be." The deeper I dig into a topic, more and more questions seem to rise to the surface; there never seem to be any clear answers.

When I embarked upon this project, my primary goal was to expose the "Control System" behind the convoluted series of healthcare reforms that have been promoted over the past several decades. The healthcare plan proposed by Hillary Clinton back in 1993, for all its claims to respond to a groundswell from the people, was the epitome of top-down reform. The driving force behind what eventually was enacted under the name "Obamacare" is a group comprised of members of the economic and social elites, and among the primary intended beneficiaries of the program are the large insurance companies and drug conglomerates.

The army of the uninsured, many of whose members will undoubtedly benefit to some degree, are merely pawns in the larger game, which is to complete the takeover of the healthcare system by large corporations and so-called charitable trusts, a process that was initiated and greatly advanced by John D. Rockefeller, Sr., whose efforts to organize the medical education system and to promote a drug-centered ("allopathic") system of healthcare were the opening salvo in a century-long battle to control a sixth of the American economy.

While it is certainly true that President Obama was a strong advocate and the public face of healthcare reform, a review of the facts and the history surrounding the slow and tortuous path to Obamacare establishes that Barack Obama was neither the creator nor the author of the Obamacare Law. He was simply the messenger, the salesman, who was used by the Control System to sell a reform scheme involving more government regulation and involvement in the healthcare system to the American people.

Given that Obama was young, charismatic and well-spoken, he was the perfect front man for the job. He appealed to the young and the old, the rich and the poor. His historic status as the first African-American President enabled him to expand his platform across racial, socio-economic and gender lines to have his signature program of healthcare reform heard and enacted.

Obama's success in achieving passage of Obamacare in the face of powerful opposition, not least from a very large number of the American people, led many admiring media commentators to acclaim Obama as "the most consequential President since Franklin D. Roosevelt." Obama's detractors, with equal fervency, derided his plan as a threat to the capitalist system and the American way of life. The fact of the matter is that Barack Obama contributed little more than his name to the substance of the Affordable Care Act, commonly known as "Obamacare." The Obamacare Law largely duplicated the failed plan spearheaded by Hillary Clinton in the early 1990s. That plan was itself a clone of a Jimmy Carter plan, which was in turn borrowed from the idea men around Richard Nixon. The first large-scale trial of Obama's version of healthcare reform was enacted in Massachusetts under Governor Mitt Romney, and the chief intellectual inspiration for the hodge-podge of managed competition, price controls and insurance regulations we know as Obamacare was a study done by the right-wing Heritage Foundation, which saw "managed competition" as an alternative to a single-payer "socialized medicine" system.

The end result is a law that only a think tank or a billionaire healthcare tycoon could love. Obamacare's multi-level reforms have certainly succeeded at reducing the number of uninsured, but the cost-benefit analysis is a complicated matter that will keep tens of thousands of think tank experts and lobbyists employed as it spawns numerous investigations, pro and con PR campaigns, not to mention existential threats to the Republic and to special interests of all kinds.

All of this back-and-forth only serves to mask the true identities and motivations of the dark moneyed forces who have assumed control of the healthcare system in America. In this book, I will unmask some of these bad actors and their supposedly good intentions. Along the way, I will present my vision of natural healthcare alternatives.

As a Doctor of Chiropractic I understand that we must nurture nature, not destroy it. The human body is naturally adaptable, and our goal as health-care providers should be to help people maximize their innate "Adaptability Factor" so that they can live happy, healthy and productive lives.

I call this book "Generation SICK" because I think too many people, especially young people, are taking the easy way out. Participation in sports is way down in many communities, to the detriment of our health and well-being. Part of this is due to the disturbing phenomenon of sports superstars who inspire disgust among the public through actions including murder, rape, road rage, heavy drinking at strip clubs, gambling on their own teams, abusing animals, and numerous other crimes and improprieties. I am outraged by the widespread adoption of performance-enhancing drugs and energy drinks among so-called elite athletes, whose status as role models has been severely compromised by the shameful actions of stars such as Alex Rodriguez and Michael Phelps, people who should obviously know better than to abuse their bodies with harmful substances, and whose mis-deeds reverberate among our youth. The abuse of steroids and other so-called performance-enhancing drugs is a major stain on our national honor.

People are also taking the easy way out in many other critical areas of life. Junk food binges, which were not so long ago the butt of jokes, have now morphed into steady diets of junk food. Some school lunch programs now feature pizza as many as three times a week, with the other two days devoted to chicken nuggets and hot dogs. Even would-be health food nuts have fallen prey to the chemical food industry's promotion of toxic crap as healthful and nutritious. Most people don't realize that diet soda only serves to fatten them up, and that the Creamy Italian or Balsamic Vinegar salad dressing they pour on their genetically modified vegetables and bacon bits contains more salt and sugar than nearly anything else they would be likely to eat.

All this exercise deprivation and junk food translates into poor performance at work and in the bedroom. People who take the lazy way out by eating TV dinners in front of a large-screen TV are usually not averse to cutting corners at work. American manufacturing know-how and craftsmanship is now so diminished that we have mostly taken a back seat to China and Mexico and Malaysia. Researchers spend more time on Wikipedia than at the libraries. Migrant workers from Mexico and Central America pick our fruits and vegetables, clean our houses and hotels, drive our delivery trucks and passenger vehicles, and do the lion's share of the labor that would require the use of chainsaws, hammers, screwdrivers, shovels, pickaxes, or stone-cutting tools. Instead of doing an honest day's work, most Americans are involved in organized profit-making activities such as real estate sales, financial sales, law, and medical billing. The result is an ever-widening ripple of bubbles bursting, time spent on longer and longer lines, and bankruptcies, many of them caused by credit card financing of botched or unnecessary operations and life-saving procedures that did not save anybody's life.

The country is now trillions of dollars in debt, and the chief preoccupation of our policymakers is to figure out new ways to expand the entitlement system that takes care of military veterans, senior citizens, schoolchildren, the poor, the disabled, and especially the rich, who contribute so generously to our corrupt politicians and are overwhelmingly the chief beneficiaries of government largesse. Landlords suck up HUD money; Wal-Mart is the final destination of most EBT money; and Obamacare is a cash cow not only for the doctors, nurses and EMT technicians who see patients, but also for the financial conglomerates and hedge funds that own and control the large hospitals and pharmaceutical companies that receive the vast bulk of the proceeds from the hugely expensive treatment of the chronic diseases generated by our unhealthy lifestyle.

It should be clear by now that I am deeply opposed to the current policy of making the healthcare system an adjunct of the financial system. In my opinion, the prevalence of drugs in our society is an unmitigated evil. While I acknowledge that there are times when drug treatment may appear less painful or more fast-acting than known alternatives, I have found that I am mostly able to get along just fine without recourse to toxic chemicals. I do not believe that the vast increase in easy availability of prescription drugs and other controlled substances we can expect as a result of the dubious alliance of healthcare reformers and medical research institutes dominated by drug money will result in greater health and happiness among the American population.

There will be many who criticize my solutions as too simplistic, too extreme or too outmoded. I will acknowledge that the centerpiece of my healthcare recommendations, the life-saving diet promulgated by "Dr." Sebi, is controversial for legitimate reasons. Nonetheless, I am sticking with the Sebi diet because it works for me and it works for my family. I fully realize that I am swimming against the tide when I criticize practices that have become so ingrained in our society, but the other direction is full of sharks and I really don't want to swim with them.

This book is not intended to tell you what to think about the Control System, their secrets or purposes. It takes no position; it has no agenda. The information and opinions contained within simply serve as a platform for exposing facts that you may not have known. My purpose is to give you another perspective on the history of the process that led to so-called healthcare reform in America, and to propose an alternative vision based on the time-tested methods of natural healing.

I hope you will find this discussion thought-provoking, and that the ideas I raise will generate some serious conversations among your friends and family. You may make your own decisions and choose for yourself what positions to take on the many healthcare issues at hand, but I hope you will emerge with an understanding that deeper forces are involved than seems apparent at first glance; that these forces are for all intents and purposes unstoppable; and that Obamacare is as much, if not more, about plowing profits to the Control System as about improving the health of the American people.

The late actor and comedian Robin Williams (1951-2014) said it best in *The Dead Poets Society*: "Just when you think you know something, you must look at it a different way."

In one of the great ironies of our time, Williams, who personified the ideals of energy, compassion and personal integrity in so many of his wonderful TV and screen performances, epitomized the dark side of Generation SICK in his private life. He was a wonderful, giving, intelligent, witty and loving man, but he sadly allowed his body and mind to be ravaged and destroyed by the demons of alcohol and drug addiction. More than a year after his untimely death, revelations continue to pour in about the physical and mental tortures that drove this seemingly most gentle of men to suicide. Williams apparently suffered from Lewy body dementia, incipient Alzheimer's Disease, and Parkinson's Disease in addition to his well-hidden depression. If we are to make any progress at all in improving the health of our society, we need to redouble our efforts to reduce the omnipresence of over-the-counter, prescription, and illegal drugs in our national experience. It avails us nothing if all our progress in increasing life expectancy is undermined by drugs that drive people to murder, suicide and depression. You can have all the Obamacare benefits you want, but if the medical system is geared toward abetting the self-destructive and murderous tendencies of our young men and women, we are doomed as a people.

This book is a unique amalgam of entertainment, instruction, and political commentary sometimes verging into satire. I hope you enjoy reading it as much as I have enjoyed writing it, and I hope it contributes in some way to your quest to live a better and more active life. Thanks for reading!

One

"Those who manipulate the unseen mechanism of society constitute an invisible government which is the true ruling power of our country. We are governed, our minds molded, our tastes formed, our ideas suggested largely by men we never heard of. In almost every act of our lives, whether in the sphere of politics or business, in our social conduct or our ethical thinking, we are dominated by the relatively small number of persons who understand the mental processes and social patterns of the masses. It is they who pull the wires that control the public mind."

— *EDWARD BERNAYS,* PIONEER OF
CORPORATE PR AND PROPAGANDA

In politics, there is no "one-size-fits-all" solution. Where you stand depends on where you sit. Differences in economic status, ethnicity, education and dozens of other factors play large roles in determining how a person sees the world and how she votes. A glass that is half-empty is also half-full. It is your mind that tells you the difference, not the measurement. However, your view can be influenced by someone telling you that "half-full" is right, and that "half-empty" is wrong. When someone else tells you what you are seeing, it often causes you to see things differently. Similarly, manipulation of perspective can and has been used to affect your view on healthcare reform and Hillary Clinton's role in it. The unveiling of Obamacare, like the announcement of Hillarycare nearly 20 years earlier, was the product of numerous secret strategy sessions, political horse trading and compromises. The public announcements of these reform programs stressed that their goal was to increase the access of poor and struggling Americans to quality healthcare. Any controversy seemed to concern primarily the proposed increase in the government's role in the medical industry. Generally, facts about how certain specialists and certain treatments were favored over other, perhaps equally effective medical practices, as well as important facts about how insurance companies and other financial concerns came to assume priority over doctors and patients, were left out of most accounts of how the system was intended to work.

The only side the mainstream media seems to present to the American public is the side the government wants you to see. And the sad truth is that the mainstream media includes the so-called alternative media outlets such as Fox News and the like. All of these media companies are owned by tycoons who see these investments in media as a means to promote their financial interests, which more often than not include healthcare stock portfolios. Instead of a robust debate about what kind of treatments and medical procedures promote the health of the American people, we were treated to a sideshow about whether Obamacare is a socialist plot or too focused on the bottom line of insurance companies.

Whether under the Obamacare regime or under the old system, the hidden true story of the state of American health is that it just keeps getting worse and worse in ways that are apparent to all. Radiation therapies, powerful pills with toxic side effects, obesity, poor posture, the widespread availability of libido enhancers, mood control pills, and even medical marijuana are all indicators that things could not be much worse. Life expectancy is rising more slowly among Americans, and is accompanied by a rapid decline in the quality of life in most of the country.

For Obamacare successfully to become law where Hillarycare failed, a healthcare crisis situation had to be created. The propaganda machine worked overtime to create the illusion of a major healthcare crisis in America, so major that the public would cry out for reform. Was there really a healthcare crisis in America? And if so, did we really need *this* type of reform to address it?

Many people took the point of view that there was no healthcare crisis, and that America enjoyed the privileges and benefits of the greatest healthcare system anywhere in the world. In his May 9, 1993 *Richmond Times-Dispatch* column, Fred Barnes exposed the "national myth of the health care crisis." Barnes stated, "Most opinion polls show three-quarters of Americans are satisfied with the health care they receive...There is no health care crisis." Barnes goes on to accuse the press of "trumpeting the crisis theme." According to Barnes' article, our healthcare problems stem from such problems as AIDS, crack cocaine babies ($125,000 each) and the cost of emergency treatment for indigent citizens. Barnes revealed that American hospitals at the time were providing $10 billion annually in uncompensated care to those who can't pay. He concludes his article by stating, "In truth, the U.S. has little but painful lessons to learn from the health-care experiences of other countries. There's practically nothing to emulate."

So is the glass half-empty or half-full when it comes to discussing the issue of the alleged "healthcare crisis" in America? I would simply note that this is a complex question, and readers should make up their own minds about it.

Whether the crisis was real or invented, the solutions foisted upon us both by the huge insurance companies and other financial backers profiting from Obamacare, and by the billionaire plutocrats backing the nonexistent Republican alternative to Obamacare, do little to address the most important healthcare needs of the American people.

The government role in the healthcare system is determined by the wishes of Big Finance. Which party runs the government makes little difference. The Democrats behind Obamacare will have a marginal impact on improving care for the small minority of people who had been unable for financial reasons regularly to see a doctor, while sucking money from taxpayers to subsidize millions of useless operations, ineffective treatments, and medicines that make people sicker. The end result is piles of money for insurance underwriters, pharmaceutical companies and pathology labs. More and more people will hear the unwelcome news that "the operation was a success, but the patient died."

Putting Republicans in charge of healthcare would be just as bad, indeed probably much worse. While the taxpayer burdens might go down slightly, the social cost of bankruptcies due to unforeseen or exorbitant medical expenses, the rise in mortality from easily treated and contagious conditions, and the failure represented by over-reliance on the hospital emergency room, would continue to ravage our society. There is, of course, one group that would be happy with such an outcome. This would be an important segment of the bankers who control access to credit and healthcare. That is why this debate is still ongoing: the bankers who fund the political process cannot agree on how best to line their pockets.

It was a long struggle, but the proponents of healthcare reform triumphed over the do-nothing Pollyannas of the Republican opposition.

Unfortunately, although some people will certainly find themselves in a better place, the people who benefit the most will be the usual suspects.

What people have been told, but do not fully appreciate, is that Obamacare is a Republican idea. It was hatched and pollinated in think tanks established by the Rockefeller family. It is a well-known fact that the right-wing Heritage Foundation, which now goes all out to condemn Obamacare, also has pride of place as the institution that created many of the specific elements of Obama's plan, such as the individual and employer mandates now so unpopular with the Republican base. Had Obama been defeated, we would have gotten the same policy under a different name. McCare or Romneycare might have tried to achieve less ambitious results, but there was no turning the tide of healthcare reform once the Control System decided that was the prescription we needed.

The Control System always relies on a simple game plan. That game plan is: create a problem, wait for the public to react and then provide them with a solution to the problem that the Control System created in the first place. In the case of Obamacare, the creation of the artificial health-care crisis served as the Problem. The uproar of the American people, many of whom were calling for reform of the healthcare system after being bombarded with stories and propaganda carefully calculated to make them uncomfortable with the status quo, constituted the Reaction. The passing into law of the Affordable Care Act in 2010 under the leadership of President Barack Obama was the Solution. This was the same method used by The Control System to bring into law the Federal Reserve Act of 1913 and take over control of the American financial system. The financial crisis at the time was said to also be created and propagated by the press.

Bankers, not politicians, have the ultimate say in what happens in America. The elite capitalists and financiers are well aware of the need to create an illusion of social progress. That's how we got the Income Tax; that's how we got Social Security; that's how we got Medicare. That's how we keep getting into wars. While all of these things may have some considerable benefits for society, none of them happen without the agitation and support of powerful financial interests.

While the Control System includes many bankers, financial institutions have by now figured out more efficient ways of making money than just issuing credit cards and foreclosing on the homes and business of deadbeats. The big banks finance and dominate industries ranging from insurance and IT to energy and logistics. All of these investments are enhanced by the flow of money into the healthcare system, which by most estimates currently represents about one-sixth of the American economy. More hospitals, more drugs, more computers, and more robotic surgeries – all this puts more money into the hands of investors in the financial sector. That is why the Control System has put so much effort into encouraging healthcare infrastructure development and healthcare reform. At this point, there is no turning back. Now let's see how new Republican President, Donald Trump handles thing?

Two

*"Just look at us. Everything is backwards: everything is upside
down. Doctors destroy health, lawyers destroy justice, universities
destroy knowledge, governments destroy freedom, the major
media destroy information and religions destroy spirituality."*

— *Michael Ellner*

The Hippocratic Oath serves as a reminder to the newly graduated
Medical Doctors of their purpose and duty as health care professionals, but the practices of the medical profession today have little to do with
the teachings and practices of Hippocrates. Hippocrates was a "naturopathic" physician who used natural techniques and natural substances such
as herbs to treat and cure disease. Most doctors today have been trained
and indoctrinated into a system we can call "allopathic" medicine, which
promotes the widespread use of artificial, chemical-based drugs and surgical treatments rather than relying on "the wisdom of the body" to right itself when confronted by disease. The name and image of Hippocrates has
been used as a smokescreen to hide the real purposes of modern medicine
men and their allopathic system of medical care.

During the last century, it is certainly true that major strides have been made in improving longevity and public health. While this progress is undeniable, the cause of this improvement is a matter of some controversy. While some surgical techniques and wonder drugs such as penicillin have justly made their inventors and discoverers known as benefactors of humanity, it has also been rightly pointed out that much of the improvement in quality and quantity of life comes from such measures as improving the drinking water supply, better diet and exercise habits, smoking cessation and cutting air pollution. For all the money our society spends on painkillers, sexual stimulants and blood thinners, drugs have relatively little impact on the state of public health. Many of their benefits are counteracted by potent side effects, by the chemicals now poisoning our water supply, and by the decreasing effectiveness of drugs that have been over-prescribed. Resistance to antibiotics is just one of the better-known examples.

Naturopathic doctors understand that human beings, as part of nature, are best treated with remedies that are natural. Fresh air, sunlight, clean water, healthy non-GMO food, herbal remedies, chiropractic, massage, acupuncture and positive thinking will do more to keep a person sane and healthy than a whole pharmacy full of pills, topical solutions and test kits. This does not mean that medical information is irrelevant or that all scientific progress in medicine is useless. On the contrary, the best naturopathic physicians are careful students of the body and its reactions to the environment. They spend time getting to know their patients and building relationships with them based on the shared goal of promoting a healthy lifestyle. The main purpose of healthcare under this system is preventive medicine, i.e., keeping a person from getting so sick that he or she ends up in the hospital or forms a lifelong dependence on powerful drugs. More and more, mainstream physicians recognize that the best advice a doctor can give is to encourage patients to eat properly, to exercise regularly and seriously, and to avoid introducing unnatural and harmful substances into the body.

The allopathic model of medicine was introduced to the United States not as a healthcare system, but rather as an industrial enterprise carefully designed and engineered to provide a steady stream of profit to the great monopolists of America's Gilded Age. The medical training system we have in America today was pioneered largely in Germany, which had long been recognized as a leader in the fields of chemistry, pharmacology, medical use of radiation, surgery and hospital-building. This German model relied heavily on the use of drugs, surgical procedures and long hospital stays. It has gotten to the point that many Americans feel that a visit to the doctor has been wasted unless the patient is sent home with a pill prescription, a recommendation for a colonoscopy or a referral to an in-network specialist, who will offer an entire new menu of potent and very expensive tests and treatments.

Allopathic medicine, by which we mean the shepherding of patients to ever more expensive surgical interventions and drug therapies, is purely profit-driven. Hospitals and drug research labs are mammoth enterprises that depend on the influx of a constantly increasing supply of patient money, whether generated through greater numbers of sick people or through higher charges for procedures. Since generating profits is the main priority of the healthcare system, healing and curing the sick becomes almost an afterthought. It is often pointed out that the vast majority of the hospital care the average American receives over a lifetime occurs in the last year of her life. The longer an individual is kept sick and in a state of symptom management, the more money is generated to support the growth and expansion of the medical system.

Patients come to doctors hoping for cures; what they receive instead are "treatments," drugs or surgical procedures that sometimes are quite effective, but that all too often only serve to exacerbate or prolong the condition that sent the patient to the doctor's office. That is because curing everybody would mean dwindling need for medical services. The big money, for doctors, for hospitals, for insurance companies and for all the other players in the medical industry, is in managing chronic illnesses such as diabetes, asthma, cancer, hypochondria, epilepsy, and scores of other conditions named and unnamed.

Full understanding of the healthcare business model requires only an honest answer to a very simple question: *"If I controlled an industry that only made a profit when people are sick, then what would be my motivation to ensure that they are healthy?"* All too often, what is seen as the correct answer among those managing the healthcare system is, *"There is none."*

"Profits before patients" could be seen as the motto and driving force behind the current allopathic medical model in America today. The allopathic monopoly on healthcare has been promoted and aggravated as the result of a conspiracy that was the brainchild of the drug trust. Understanding how this came to be requires a short history lesson.

Since feudal times, most "advanced" medical treatments were available only to kings and nobles. The treatment of the poor was not encouraged. In modern times, the first documented attempt to install a medical monopoly was an Act of 1511, signed into law by King Henry VIII. This Act, which made it an offense to practice medicine without the approval of an "expert panel," is the forerunner of today's state and national medical licensing boards. King Henry VIII's Act of 1511 was permanently enshrined with the founding of the Royal College of Physicians.

King Henry's Act codified and formalized class divide among doctors, a term which at the time included barbers as well as surgeons. "Authorized" doctors treated the rich and powerful, while doctors who were now labeled "unauthorized" treated the poor. In England, harassment of the unauthorized doctors who treated the poor contributed to widespread suffering throughout the country. Within a generation, the excesses resulting from putting supervision of medical practice into the hands of a small group of wealthy doctors became apparent to the king, who during his long reign had developed considerable respect for the benefits of herbal treatments as opposed to leeches and bleeding. In reaction to surgeons and physicians who had attempted to enforce a profitable monopoly on medical care by suing unauthorized practitioners, King Henry VIII enacted an Herbalists Charter, which came to be known as the "Quacks Charter," in 1542. The purpose of this Charter was legally to exempt "unauthorized doctors" from oversight by the expert panels and thus allow them to continue to treat the sick among the poor population.

In subsequent years, medical professionals continued their efforts to enforce their standards and practices, and thereby to gain for an elite group total control over the practice of medicine. 1617 saw the creation of the Worshipful Society of Apothecaries, which was established for the purpose of challenging the College of Physicians' monopoly on practicing medicine. Naturally, the apothecaries' guild, which created what we experience today as the "general practitioner" model, attempted to create their own monopoly. They achieved this goal in 1815, when the Apothecaries Act granted the society control over licensing and regulation of medical practitioners in England.

In 1832, the British Medical Association was formed as a trade union for doctors. The BMA served as the model for the formation of the American Medical Association (AMA) in the United States. Since the creation of the American Medical Association in 1847, it has had one specific purpose: to attain and defend a complete monopoly of the practice of medicine in the United States. The AMA decided that the best way to achieve this objective would be to make allopathy the primary form of medicine among its practitioner members.

The word "allopathic" (a melding of the Greek words for "opposite" and "suffering") was coined by German physician Samuel Hahnemann (1755-1843), the founder of homeopathy, who felt that barbaric practices such as bleeding, induced vomiting, purging and use of poisons such as arsenic – practices that were widespread in Germany at the time – served only to harm patients by making them suffer unnecessary indignities and pain. The word is widely used in a pejorative sense today by advocates of natural medicine to describe a system whereby doctors are trained to perform highly invasive surgeries and strong pharmacological substances to address a patient's symptoms. Rather than going with the flow, by admitting that nature's way is the best way, the medical establishment has created a system whereby doctors have to be highly trained in order to recognize complex drug interactions, potential complications caused by issues such as tissue rejection, and the mechanics of drug pathways through the bloodstream.

Since the first commandment of medicine is the catchphrase, "first, do no harm," doctors increasingly have to be experts at managing and mitigating the damage caused to their patients by substances that are by nature toxic and highly dangerous to their patients. Doctors expected to perform such complicated types of medical treatment increasingly required advanced education at a recognized academic school of medicine. In contrast to the natural, holistic healing methods that were common in the earlier days of the Republic, American physicians increasingly relied on methods involving the heavy use of synthetic drugs, even poisons, and bleeding techniques that nearly as often killed a patient as cured her. As this new allopathic system of medicine continued to expand, the leaders of the profession found it essential to overrun and discredit any form of medical practice that did not originate from accredited medical schools and did not follow increasingly standardized procedures.

There soon developed a fierce struggle for power between two completely different approaches toward treating disease. The traditional medicine of the time focused on "nurturing nature" by using natural, organic remedies made from herbs and homeopathic agents that stimulated the body's own immune system to respond and strengthen, in the hope of curing the individual of all traces of disease. The new, German-inspired, allopathic form of medicine relied heavily on artificial drugs and radical surgeries, which in the opinion of the homeopaths and herbalists, went against the grain of all things natural and indeed offended what traditional doctors regarded as the natural laws of the healing process. Homeopaths maintained that synthetic chemicals poisoned the body and that unnecessary surgeries only introduced further trauma to a body already under stress from the fight against illness. The fight was not just over the relative merits of various medical techniques and preparations. The two sides had very different philosophies. Naturopaths/homeopaths/herbalists took the view that "health is achieved from an inside-out methodology," while the allopaths believed in an "outside-in" approach.

The dominant medical schools of the late 18th and much of the 19th centuries focused on the teaching of homeopathy, the most popular form of natural medicine. The first homeopathic school, established by Samuel Hahnemann, was based on his concept of "*similibus cyentur*" ("like cures like"). Homeopathy purports to work through direct stimulation of the immune system, using non-toxic doses of substances that are similar to those that caused the illness. The purpose of homeopathic treatment is to get your immune system to respond positively and effectively, thereby allowing your body to cure the condition naturally. Such practices, while no longer part of the standard medical toolkit, continue to have their advocates even today. Queen Elizabeth of England is probably the best-known advocate of homeopathy. Her personal physician, Dr. Peter Fisher, is a homeopath. He also treats other members of the Royal Family, including Crown Prince Charles.

In the United States, homeopathic physicians are viewed as "quacks." The medical cartel now attempts at every turn to discredit their work in the public square, but it was not so long ago that that homeopathy was considered a mainstream approach that delivered good results for many patients. Dr. George H. Simmons, who ran the American Medical Association from 1899-1924, for many years ran advertisements in Lincoln, Nebraska, where he practiced, which proudly proclaimed that he was a "homeopathic physician."

Homeopaths claimed notable success in treating major cholera epidemics in Europe, beginning with an 1831 epidemic that ravaged across Europe. Patients treated in conventional hospitals suffered mortality rates from 40% to as high as 80%; while patients treated by homeopaths died at much lower rates. In Bavaria, it was reported, only 7% of homeopathic patients died! The London Homeopathic Hospital claimed a 16.4% mortality rate during an 1854 outbreak that killed 51.8% of those treated allopathically.

Dr. Hahnemann's book, *Homeopathica Materia Medica,* made learning the art and methods of homeopathy quick and easy. As a result, in the 19th century, homeopathy spread rapidly throughout the United States and Europe. It was so popular at the height of its success that homeopathic physicians outnumbered allopathic physicians by more than two to one. In response to the rise in popularity of the homeopathic physicians, The American Medical Association (AMA) was founded as a trade lobby, for the purpose of neutralizing any competition and driving the homeopaths out of business. By the early 1900s, the AMA was able in large measure to achieve these objectives.

The AMA not only attacked the homeopathic physicians, but also attacked any practitioner who practiced any form of healing that addresses the human body as a whole, rather than taking up one part at a time. Since allopathic physicians were trained to treat symptoms and not causes of disease, every practitioner who treated causes was seen as a threat, and was thereby exposed to attacks by the AMA.

The dogmas that fueled the illusion of the superiority of the AMA-run schools of medicine can be seen clearly in the constant self-promotion of their myth that the allopathic brand of medicine was the only type that was effective in the treatment of disease. This power- and ego-driven myth was responsible for creating the "God-like" egoistic ethos of the allopathic physician. This dangerous phenomenon of the supposed omniscient physician ("I know it all. Don't question me. I don't make mistakes.") lives on today in undiminished form, although it is increasingly under attack from nurse-practitioners and patient advocates who favor a more patient-centered approach.

Ivan Ilyich, in his 1976 book *Medical Nemesis, the Expropriation of Health,* points out that the vaunted effectiveness of the allopathic school of medicine proved to be pure mythology and propaganda. Not only did doctors fail in stemming the rising tide of chronic disease; even more disastrously, allopathic doctors brought new plagues into being, illnesses which Ilyich defines as "iatrogenic." He defines iatrogenic disease as an "illness which is caused by a doctor's medical intervention." Ilyich goes on to define three commonly encountered types of iatrogenesis: clinical iatrogenesis, which he defines as "a doctor-made illness"; social iatrogenesis, which " is deliberately created by the mechanization of the medical-industrial complex";

and cultural iatrogenesis, which he states, "saps the people's will to survive." Ilyich claims that this iatrogenesis plague is now sweeping the nation.

One in twenty-five hospital patients nationwide acquire hospital-borne infections during their treatment. The problem is particularly acute in people who have to endure long-term stays. The rate of medical mistakes is so high that malpractice rates in some specialties are prohibitively expensive. Dr. Atul Gawande, a leading surgeon who has written critically of his profession, has called for the adoption of a "checklist" system to ensure that fewer patients discover in the recovery room that the wrong lung has been removed, or that the wrong leg was amputated.

We are indoctrinated from childhood with the idea that we should blindly trust medical doctors. But how can this trust survive intact when, all too often, the professional who supposedly has been trained to heal you has been exposed as the same person who is now responsible for making you sick?

In its continued strive for power and control over the citizens of the United States, the AMA continues to push its claims that medical care has improved, and that it is largely as a result of their efforts that the health and longevity of American citizens has also improved. Historical records show otherwise and debunk many of these claims. There is plenty of evidence to support the idea that as a result of allopathic medical intervention, the health of the American people has declined in many respects.

Advances that did occur were often in spite of the doctors whose mortality rates declined. Ignaz Semmelweis fought a losing battle to get doctors to wash and disinfect their hands prior to treating patients in maternity wards. Even after he showed that deaths from "childbed fever" declined from as high as 35% to as little as 1% among doctors taking this simple precaution, his failure to explain why this should be so meant that his work was mostly ignored. He was derided as a crank, and never lived to see the wide adoption of hand washing that took place some years after his untimely death, which occurred just 14 days after he was committed to an asylum.

Some argue that mortality rates from infectious diseases such as tuberculosis began their steep declines long before the introduction of vaccines and antibiotics. Late in the 19th century, it is estimated that 80% or more of the urban population in Europe and the United States was infected with the TB bacillus. Developing active TB was a death sentence: 80% of patients died from the disease. Poor sanitation and high population density contributed greatly to the spread of TB. As conditions improved due to the introduction of public health measures such as the introduction of running water and indoor plumbing to homes; the discouragement of spitting in the streets; and isolation of TB patients from the general population, rates began to fall. Thanks in large measure to the pioneering work of Robert Koch and the development of antibiotics, TB has been nearly eliminated in the United States.

The effectiveness of antibiotics in the fight against TB has been proclaimed one of medical history's greatest success stories, but a balanced look at the history of TB treatment reveals that this is not a case of either/or. Homeopathic doctors dominated the American landscape in the 19th century, and as we have seen, the medical community, working with public health authorities, had already made considerable headway in reducing the toll from TB long before Koch succeeded in identifying its cause.

Increasingly, we face the threat of drug-resistant strains of TB. In 2014, the National Institutes of Health (NIH) released a report on a study in India, where it was found that homeopathic treatment appeared to have some effectiveness when drugs were not working. The conclusion of the NIH report was that the use of homeopathy as an adjunct to traditional drug therapy merits further study.

The story with other infectious diseases, from whooping cough and diphtheria to polio, is much the same. Despite all the progress medical science has made since Pasteur and Koch established the germ theory of disease, we are still groping for effective treatments for cancer, heart disease, diabetes, and scores of other major chronic diseases. It often seems as if we take two steps back for every step forward. In place of the $5 home remedy or the sip of brandy that often did the trick for our grandparents, we now have thousand-dollar pills and hospital bills that bankrupt families. Are these modern treatments really a thousand times better, or are there other reasons that medical expenses absorb so much of our personal and national income?

The rise in the ranks of the medical profession has been steady and impressive. In 1900, there was one doctor for every 750 Americans; today, there are two or three per thousand, depending on the region. How and why did this growth occur, even while many of the diseases that formerly occupied our physicians have been decimated or even eradicated?

Medical training at the beginning of the 20th century generally consisted of a two year apprenticeship, after which most doctors earned roughly the same salary as a good mechanic. With the salary of a physician so low given the demands of the profession, it was hard to recruit and retain doctors. For the medical industry to grow and prosper, it was essential to present the profession as a lucrative one. The man who took on this job was Dr. George H. Simmons, the homeopath editor of the American Medical Association Journal in 1900, who proclaimed, "The growth of the profession must be stemmed if the individual members are to find the practice of medicine a lucrative profession."

Once he decided on his goal of cutting the number of doctors in order to elevate salaries, Dr. Simmons had the great good fortune of attracting the sympathy to his cause of the world's richest man, John D. Rockefeller, the semi-retired and notorious billionaire head of Standard Oil, who had deputized Baptist clergyman Frederick T. Gates, his most important business advisor, as his "agent for philanthropic endeavors" and was looking to get involved in the medical field. It has been suggested that Rockefeller saw the medical field not as an opportunity to distribute his largesse for the benefit of American society, but rather a chance to increase his prestige, his wealth and his power by creating a monopoly over the healthcare system that had the potential to bring in more revenue than the oil business. While this never quite came to pass during his lifetime, it must be acknowledged that the impact of Rockefeller's investments in medical research, medical education and the American hospital system represents one of his enduring legacies.

Rockefeller, like most men of his time, believed in home remedies and homeopathic medicine. He was the son of a con artist and snake-oil salesman who traveled around the small-town circuit selling miracle cures. Bill Rockefeller famously bragged, "I cheat my sons every chance I get. I want to make them sharp." Ron Chernow, John D. Rockefeller's biographer, suggested that the key to understanding Rockefeller's life was to see everything he did as a reaction against his father.

By the end of his life, John D. Rockefeller had devoted more than half a billion dollars to charity. Biographer Chernow flatly calls him "the greatest philanthropist in history." The fact that much of that investment went to the causes of medical research and education rather than to the Baptist Church was in large part due to the acumen of Frederick Gates, who pushed Rockefeller in a direction that could not have been foreseen.

Rockefeller considered Frederick Gates the greatest businessman he knew, and valued him over such other magnates such as Andrew Carnegie and even Henry Ford, whose promotion of the internal combustion engine arguably was the greatest single factor in making Rockefeller the richest man on Earth. After being appointed head of philanthropy, Gates went right to work creating a strategy that would lay the cornerstone for the Rockefeller medical monopoly.

Gates presented Rockefeller with a plan to dominate the entire medical education system within the United States. This plan took concrete form with the creation of the Rockefeller Institute of Medical Research, still one of the world's leading medical research establishments. The next step occurred in 1907, when the AMA requested that the Carnegie Foundation conduct a survey of all the medical schools in the country. The Carnegie Foundation appointed education reformer Abraham Flexner, who had published a critical report on the state of college education in 1908, and who is perhaps best known today as the founder of Princeton's Institute of Advanced Research, academic home to Albert Einstein in his later years, to head the study of the medical schools for the AMA. The resulting *Flexner Report* was published in 1910. Simon Flexner, Abraham's brother, who had studied pathology and then served as a professor of medicine at Johns Hopkins University, was by that time the head of the Rockefeller Institute of Medical Research. He worked closely with his brother on conducting this research on medical education.

It seems that the person who had the greatest impact on the *Flexner Report* may have been the long-time president of the Johns Hopkins University, Daniel Coit Gilman (1831-1908), a leading member of the Rockefeller General Education Board who had recently died. Gilman had led the Carnegie Institute, a center of science education in Washington, D.C., as its first president following his retirement from Johns Hopkins.

Gilman believed in the German model of advanced education, and his inauguration as JHU president is often said to mark the beginning of graduate school training in the United States.

Gilman, a Yale graduate, had been an active member of the Skull and Bones Society, an elite group whose ranks have included many distinguished Americans, including both Presidents Bush. Gilman later co-founded the Russell Sage Foundation in order to finance the activities of Skull and Bones. These activities, which are secret, have been construed by some to include plots to dominate the world by promoting members of the Yale elite. During the first George Bush administration, Bush's use of the catchphrase "New World Order" in reference to the opportunities presented by a post-Cold War world, was taken by some on the Fundamentalist Christian right, notably former Republican candidate Pat Robertson, as a signal that Bush was a front man for the planned establishment of an authoritarian one-world government run by the United Nations. The Persian Gulf War against Saddam Hussein's Iraq, which involved a huge coalition of countries and was financed largely by Saudi Arabia, added fuel to the fire. Now that a third Bush family member, who developed his political career as "an education reformer," has declared his interest in pursuing the Presidency, with one of the chief obstacles in his path being Yale Law graduate and former First Lady Hillary Clinton, it is hard to avoid the impression that someone is stacking the deck in favor of the political equivalent of the Five Families!

Sinister or not, it cannot be denied that Skull and Bones alumni have been famously active in the highest reaches of American society. William Howard Taft, whose father had founded the society, was President of the United States at the time the Flexner Report appeared.

During Gilman's long career in education, he would act as a founder, executive officer and/or board member for many of the charitable trusts that formed the basis for what eventually became the Rockefeller Foundation. He was a trustee of the John F. Slater and Peabody Education Funds, which eventually merged with Rockefeller's Southern Education Fund to become the "General Education Fund," whose mission was to reform education across the United States. Among the pet causes of the GEF were women's education and black education. Spelman College, one of the leading centers for the education of African-American women in the United States, located in Atlanta, Georgia is named for John D. Rockefeller's abolitionist wife, Laura Spelman Rockefeller. Rockefeller was so impressed when he first visited the college that he paid off its debt and financed the construction of its main building, now known as Rockefeller Hall. Alumni of Spelman College, which is sometimes called "the Radcliffe of the South," include novelist Alice Walker and children's advocate Marian Wright Edelman.

Gilman recruited several fellow Bonesmen to teach at the Johns Hopkins Medical School. Among these were William Henry Welch, a dominant figure in American medical education for 50 years; William Stewart Halstead, JHU's first professor of surgery, who has been called "the most important figure in the history of surgery in America"; and Harvey Williams Cushing, the pioneering neurosurgeon.

Abraham Flexner was thoroughly familiar with the German-derived Johns Hopkins educational model implemented under Gilman: JHU was Flexner's alma mater. Flexner later wrote an admiring biography of Gilman, a biography in which he carefully avoids any mention of Skull and Bones or the infamous *Illuminati,* with whom Gilman allegedly had deep connections.

Flexner needed no convincing on the superior merits of the German educational system. His parents had emigrated from Germany, and he had traveled and studied in Germany as a young man. The Flexner Report made the case that allopathic medicine and the German model of advanced clinical training offered the best hope for the future of American medicine. Conveniently, raising the standards of medical education in this way raised huge barriers to entry into the medical profession. This was fine with Rockefeller, whose hope for a monopoly on medical education depended on weeding out competition. Flexner's conclusions were perfectly aligned with these interests: "Reckless overproduction of cheap doctors has resulted in general over-crowding. It appears, then, that the country needs fewer and better doctors; and that the way to get the better is to produce fewer."

Flexner presented a solution that would make medical education so elite, expensive and drawn-out that few would consider medicine as a career in the future. To achieve this purpose, Flexner set up strict requirements that consisted of four years of undergraduate college, followed by a further four years of medical school. Two-year apprenticeships would no longer suffice. The Flexner Report stated that medical schools now must have expensive laboratories and equipment. As a result of the drastic changes that were implemented by The Flexner Report, the number of medical schools in the United States rapidly declined, from 650 to only 50 in a matter of a few years. Annual graduation numbers were reduced from 7500 to only 2500. This great reduction ensured that the medical monopoly in the United States would create, by design, a very small group of elite students from affluent families.

The surprise down side for this new, small, elite group of allopathic medical doctors is that they would now be subject to intense controls, overseen by the Rockefeller Foundation in partnership with the AMA, state medical boards, and the government of the United States. Over the next few years, the AMA successfully lobbied for the creation of the United

States Public Health Services, which consolidated all the public health agencies of the United States government into a single entity. This did not happen without a fight. The National League for Medical Freedom, a group lobbying for the interests of homeopaths, patent medicine sellers, and alternative healers, had successfully defeated a Congressional attempt to create a large Department of Health just a year or so earlier.

The Rockefeller Foundation had started working on joint projects with the U.S. Public Health Services from before the time the agency was officially chartered. This cooperation in the management of typhus, ringworm and other diseases was one of the earliest examples in the series of "public-private partnerships" that has come to dominate the landscape not only in the healthcare field, but even more prominently in defense contracting and procurement.

Rockefeller's good friend, legendary financier J.P. Morgan, had single-handedly engineered the bailout of the United States government in the wake of the Panic of 1907. Within just a few years, John D. Rockefeller, who had contributed millions of dollars to Morgan's heroic effort, was able to leverage the full faith and credit of the United States on behalf of his pet projects on medical education and research.

Today, everyone knows that if you want to influence the government, you do it through a think tank; if you want to get a government grant, you apply through a foundation. In no field other than national defense are the dollars and the stakes higher than the fields of healthcare and education.

By co-opting the government for his purposes in the way I have described, John D. Rockefeller established a system that has come to characterize the United States government more than anything that is written in the Constitution. The bottom line is that the richest man in the world figured out to use your money to achieve his purposes, and that his family and the successors of his cronies are still making hay by his brilliant methods nearly 80 years after his death.

The United States of America today is the land of the 1%, a place where the rich easily evade taxes by establishing family foundations and other organizations that serve their interests. This battle has been largely waged and won on behalf of the plutocrats by having their front men (and women) advocate for and against healthcare reform. By making it all about improving medical education, expanding access to community healthcare, and funneling research dollars into supposedly life-saving drugs, the folks at the top of the pyramid have accumulated obscene amounts of wealth.

Remember Mitt Romney's mansion with its special car elevator? That's only the tip of the iceberg. As our children sink deeper and deeper into dependence on bad GMO foods and bad medicines, we can expect to see many more car elevators, high-tech robot dogs and automatic flying mailboxes featured in the pages of GQ Magazine, alongside the obligatory features about President Donald Trump's new commercial building or golf course.

Three

WHY HILLARY COULD HAVE BEEN PRESIDENT?

> *"Gradually, by selective breeding, the congenital difference*
> *between rulers and ruled will increase until they become*
> *almost different species. A revolt of the plebs would*
> *become as unthinkable as an organized insurrection*
> *of sheep against the practice of eating mutton."*
>
> *"Diet, injections, and injunctions will combine, from a very early*
> *age, to produce a sort of character and the sort of beliefs that*
> *the authorities consider desirable, and any serious criticism of*
> *the powers that be will become psychologically impossible."*
>
> — **BERTRAND RUSSELL,** THE IMPACT OF
> SCIENCE ON SOCIETY *(1953)* PAGES *49-50*

Americans are proud to live in a democracy, where the idea of royal families and dictators is alien to our system. We don't want to live under the thumb of Windsors or Fuehrers or Romanovs or Putins.

In Russia, Vladimir Putin was installed as President in a coup by the same oligarchs who had managed to get a drunk, sick, oblivious old man re-elected President just a few years before by taking control of the media apparatus to present Boris Yeltsin as a vigorous dancer and party animal. Putin ran the government for the two terms prescribed in the Russian Constitution, then stepped aside in favor of a young unknown, Dmitri Medvedev, who quickly became the friendly face of Russian liberalization. During Medvedev's entire term, Putin ran Russia from behind the scenes as Prime Minister. To no one's surprise, Medvedev did not run again, but deferred to Putin, who now rules Russia with an iron fist. Opponents of the regime face death by poison or bullets in central Moscow. Many of the great oligarchs of the 1990s quickly found themselves dispossessed, imprisoned and/or exiled as Putin installed his favorites as governors and managers of giant state enterprises. More recently, Putin has taken steps to maintain Russian control over the fate of Ukraine, defying all attempts by outside powers to get him to rein in his territorial and economic ambitions.

As Americans, we offer humble thanks to the Lord that such things can't happen here. The Presidency is not a prize to be handed from one wealthy family to another. In America, we have such a vibrant democracy that the voice of the people in 2008 elected a first-term Illinois Senator, Barack Obama, as our national leader. Soon after taking office, Obama began pulling thousands of troops out of Iraq and Afghanistan. After saving the economy from Depression by a stimulus package he fought hard to get through Congress, Obama pushed through a health insurance program that provided strong protections to American citizens.

Under Obamacare, insurance companies could no longer discriminate against people with pre-existing conditions. Parents could keep children on their insurance until kids turned 26. Insurance is no longer rooted strictly to employment. People who change jobs can now keep their insurance. Contraception and women's health issues are required elements of every plan. There are new protections for seniors, for consumers, and for electoral focus group of all kinds. Only ignorant people and carping Republicans could find anything not to like. For liberals, the passage of the Affordable Care Act marked the fulfillment of a national dream. Teddy Kennedy, the last surviving member of a trio of brothers who had dominated national political life for a "brief shining moment," had fought for the passage of nationalized health insurance for decades. In a strange twist, Kennedy's death in August 2009 nearly scuttled Obamacare, but the President's brilliant advisors figured out a strategy to enact the plan into law without the need for another vote in the Senate.

If American history ended today, the Presidency of Barack Obama would be a fitting coda to our national drama. Obama was no mere white-bread Everyman like owl-eyed Harry Truman or peanut farmer Jimmy Carter. He was an African-American Everyman whose story proved conclusively that anyone could become President of the United States. Where Skull and Bones man George W. Bush unconvincingly tried to pass himself off as "the Education President," Barack Obama led by example. He was not just smart, he was Einstein smart. Obama had studied at Columbia College, at the same New York City-based Ivy League university where both President Roosevelts had gone to law school, and where Dwight D. Eisenhower had been president after leading the Allies to victory and before becoming President of the United States. Obama's life is an object lesson in the American ideal that *education*, not wealth or privilege, is the key to success. Obama's stellar grades at Columbia, where a reliably-sourced legend has it that he was the only undergraduate to receive an "A" in Zbigniew Brzezinski's "American Foreign Policy" class, earned him a place at Harvard Law School, the same university where both President Roosevelts had studied as undergraduates, and where Barack Obama achieved the distinction of being named the first African-American editor of the prestigious *Harvard Law Review*. After completing law school, Obama worked for a time as a community organizer and taught Constitutional law at the University of Chicago, the elite institution founded by oil magnate John D. Rockefeller, which has a proud tradition as the greatest and most venerable university of the Midwest. Obama distinguished himself as a best-selling writer with a distinctive voice. The audiobook of his memoir, *Dreams of My Father,* is one of the most popular tools for foreigners and new immigrants trying to learn English as a second language. Obama's time in the Senate was short, but it was clear he was a man marked for greatness. He had barely finished his first Inaugural Address when he found himself accepting the Nobel Peace Prize, thereby joining the exalted company of Theodore Roosevelt, Woodrow Wilson, Jimmy Carter and Al Gore.

Many of us were surprised that Obama was able to triumph in the battle for the 2008 Democratic Presidential nod over Hillary Clinton, the representative of a great political family. Her husband, Bill Clinton, probably did himself no favors with the Mount Rushmore Selection Committee when he chose to place his manhood in the eager mouth of a young intern, but aside from that famous stain on Monica Lewinsky's blue dress, Bill Clinton's record as Chief Executive was nearly unblemished. During this blessed interregnum between the troubled Bush years, the United States had enjoyed a period of peace and prosperity unknown since the salad days of Ronald Reagan. Indeed, Clinton's record on GDP growth and job creation was even better than Reagan's.

Actually, come to think of it, there was one wrinkle in Clinton's otherwise very successful run of policy successes. Ironically, the most conspicuous failure of his administration was the collapse of Hillarycare, the First Lady's only major venture outside the traditional women's realm of cookie baking contests and public promotion of women's rights and children's rights.

I doubt that I am the only person to suspect that Clinton's premature withdrawal from the presidential race in 2008 was the result of some backroom dealing between the candidates and their political handlers. My gut instinct told me that Hillary's time offstage would be brief. In the event, President Obama recruited her as the top Cabinet Officer in his Administration. As Secretary of State, Hillary Clinton did a lot of traveling, and was famously photographed in the White House Situation Room as part of the group monitoring the Seal Team operation to kill Osama bin Laden. She also found herself embroiled in somewhat of a tempest in a teapot controversy over the details of her arms-distance involvement in the Administration's failure to convey strongly enough that a savage al-Qaeda-inspired attack on the U.S. Embassy in Benghazi, Libya was an act of terrorism.

Hillary Clinton, having established her foreign policy credentials and having helped her husband add well over $100 million to the family bank balances by making well-paid speeches to business groups and charities, worked hard to get herself elected in 2016. We all know that she lost to Donald Trump, but the stage on the surface looked to be set for her to become the next President of the United States after Obama.

Here is the back story as I see it: Going back to the Putin/Medvedev analogy, where rich oligarchs controlling the country called the shots, which of course could not happen here, it is tempting to think about Obama as a placeholder for Hillary Clinton. The key to this analysis is the recognition that Hillarycare and Obamacare are basically identical. The Obamacare law may have twice as many pages as the Hillarycare proposal, but few pages of either of these huge tomes reveal much about the healthcare reform's hidden purposes, which basically involve creating a playing field that favors players in the financial system over ordinary members of the public. It has been pointed out here already that the Control System, by which I mean the panoply of forces centered on the Rockefeller family and its allies, has a vested and long-established interest in controlling the healthcare system. Hillary Clinton has also had a long-standing interest in the healthcare system, dating from her second year at Yale Law School, when she volunteered to work with victims of child abuse at New Haven Hospital.

Since the 1970s, when Hillary Clinton was working with the Select Committee on Impeachment to oust Rockefeller family nemesis Richard Nixon from the White House, a core group of dedicated healthcare reformers have been meeting at the home of Dr. Paul M. Ellwood in Jackson Hole, Wyoming. Dr. Ellwood, a pediatric neurologist, is best known today as one of the people who introduced the HMO concept. One of the regular members of his circle, Alain C. Enthoven, a professor of economics at Stanford University, came up with the idea of "managed competition," which became the basis of Romneycare, Hillarycare, and Obamacare. Ira Magaziner, Hillary's main advisor on healthcare, was a regular at the Jackson Hole meetings as he formulated her plan. At the time of its announcement, Hillarycare was derided as the "Insurance Industry Preservation Act," which is, unsurprisingly, how many people see Obamacare.

The two healthcare laws ran into the thousands of pages not only because of the wide-ranging powers these laws assume over so many institutions and people, but also because it is easy to hide certain uncomfortable facts in a thicket of policy wonk-style bureaucratese. One such uncomfortable fact is that Jackson Hole is Rockefeller country. During the 1930's, John D. Rockefeller, Jr. bought up vast tracts of land in and around Jackson Hole for incorporation into the Grand Tetons National Park, which is connected to Yellowstone Park, the jewel of the National Park system just 10 miles away, by the John D. Rockefeller Memorial Parkway.

Alain Enthoven began his career as an economist at the RAND Corporation, "a non-profit institution that helps improve policy and decision making through research and analysis." The RAND Corporation, which was originally formed to provide analysis for the armed services, is closely modeled on the think tanks established by the Rockefeller family, and is currently engaged in a number of collaborative research projects with the Rockefeller Foundation. Enthoven was subsequently appointed to work with Robert McNamara as Assistant Secretary of Defense. Following his stint at the heart of the military-industrial complex, this "Whiz Kid" joined Litton Industries, where he soon became president of Litton Medical Products.

Professor Enthoven's first attempt to pass healthcare reform was the Consumer Choice Health Plan he drafted while working as a consultant for President Jimmy Carter in 1977. This plan, according to Enhoven's Stanford bio, was "a plan for universal health insurance based on managed competition in the private sector."

In drafting his plan for Cartercare, a plan that became the basis for Romneycare, Hillarycare and Obamacare, Enthoven met with representatives of the Prudential, Aetna, New York Life, Cigna and Metropolitan insurance companies. These plans created in secret meetings by healthcare insiders have one major point in common: they expand the government role in healthcare, while (even more importantly) providing great opportunities for the financiers behind medical institutions and insurance companies to make a lot of money. It is a win-win, and implementation of this project must be handled smoothly. This is a top priority of the Control System. With trillions of dollars riding on this calculation, Hillary Clinton has been recognized by the powers-that-be in the Shadow Government as the person best placed to implement Obamacare, the final pieces of which take full effect in 2017, the year of her widely-anticipated inauguration as the first female President of the United States. Unfortunately for her, the American people have spoken and have elected Donald Trump as the 45th President of the United States, not Hillary Clinton. It will be interesting to see exactly what role Donald Trump plays in this agenda? As with all things, only time will tell.

Four

HILLARY CLINTON: THE QUEEN OF HEALTHCARE REFORM

> *"When you see that in order to produce, you need to obtain permission from men who produce nothing – When you see that money is flowing to those who deal, not in goods, but in favors – When you see that men get richer by graft and by pull than by work, and your laws don't protect you against them, but rather protect them against you – When you see corruption being rewarded and honesty becoming a self-sacrifice – You may know that your society is doomed."*
>
> — *AYN RAND, ATLAS SHRUGGED, 1957*

While researching this book, I've often found myself asking the question, "Why was Hillary Clinton chosen as the spear thrower/public face/water carrier/scapegoat of Health Care Reform?" Most people thought the answer was pure and simple spousal nepotism. Whatever her other merits or charms might be, her main qualification was being married to the President.

During the 1992 campaign, Hillary was presented as the epitome of modern working womanhood. Voting for Bill Clinton would get you "two for one." What a great deal! Sadly for the prospects of healthcare reform, most people didn't buy that idea. They did not see Hillary as the brilliant corporate lawyer from Yale Law School. They saw her as a "stand by your man" Southern belle (or *bête*, depending on your political persuasion and your standards of feminine beauty) who was out of her depth in taking on policy issues totally unrelated to her hospitality and ceremonial duties as First Lady. In the House and Senate, the attitude toward Hillary Clinton was even worse. The Republicans and most of the conservative Southern Democrats had no use for a shrill liberal lawyer whose only experience in government was her work trying to tear down Nixon over Watergate.

Like many others, I felt that Bill Clinton's idea to delegate healthcare policy formulation to his wife was a foolish choice. In retrospect, I was wrong. Hillary Clinton was exactly the right person for the job of implementing Rockefeller-style healthcare reform. It wasn't just the President who sponsored her. She knew all the right people, and she could be counted on to do all the right things.

The Health Care Reform Plan that carried her name on it was not a "putting people first" plan. It was never intended to be. Hillarycare is a corporate plan sponsored by the big five insurance companies. Hillary Clinton, who had worked as a corporate lawyer – she was the first female partner at Arkansas' prestigious Rose law firm – after being graduated from Yale Law School, understood corporate law and was quite comfortable with the fact that the proposed Health Care Reform Plan was a corporate bill. The Control System needed someone with the ability and experience to protect the corporations, not an advocate for the people. In Hillary Clinton, they got two for one. Hillary was not a run-of-the-mill corporate flack; she was one of the best corporate lawyers in the country, recognized as such twice by *The National Law Journal,* which featured her on its annual list of America's top 100 lawyers. Hillary Clinton had served on the Board of Directors of Wal-Mart, America's largest corporation. She understood that the healthcare plan the nation needed would be an extension of the 1913 Federal Reserve Act spearheaded by John D. Rockefeller, J.P. Morgan and their fellow industrialists and bankers. She also knew how to present the plan in a way that made it seem that it was all about defending women and children and senior citizens.

The Jackson Hole group led by Enthoven had chosen to model their healthcare Plan after the Federal Reserve Act because such a system would allow the corporations to take control of the volume and flow of currency within the system. This was important, because without this ability the entire system would spin out of control very quickly. Where does the cash flow that keeps the entire system afloat come from? It comes from the American people (and their employers) who pay their insurance premiums every month. That keeps the system working and is the only source of cash flow it has. The insurance companies need all the health care money paid directly to them to keep the system moving forward. This is why the new Obamacare Law makes health care coverage mandatory. Young and healthy people need to be enrolled not so much for their own protection, but more importantly, because the insurance companies need their premium money to continue feeding the system and keeping it from collapsing. Due to its structural problems, which include fragile employer-based system, differing coverage regulations among the states, and tort laws that necessitate huge set-asides to pay settlements on malpractice and wrongful death claims, the American healthcare system is always on the verge of collapse. The Hillary Clinton healthcare reform plan hoped to keep it together. Only the future will tell how Donald Trump's healthcare plan plays out? As will all things in Washington, DC, it's always about the "policy" not the politician. Even though Hillary lost the campaign, her policies are still intact. The fact of the matter is, the "Hidden Hand of Power" still calls the shots and the American public still loses regardless of who is President. I don't believe Trumpcare will be much different than Hillarycare.

Hillary's healthcare reform plan was sponsored in Congress by Senator John D. ("Jay") Rockefeller IV, John D. Rockefeller's namesake great-grandson, who was the only member of the Rockefeller dynasty to achieve high elective office as a Democrat. For reasons we alluded to at the beginning of this chapter, the plan failed spectacularly.

Hillary did not give up, but continued to chip away at the problem. She vacationed with her family at Jay Rockefeller's Jackson Hole ranch in 1995. The healthcare reform forces regrouped and tried to pass her plan one piece at a time. Their first success was passage of the State Children's Health Insurance Program, sponsored by Senator Edward Kennedy in the Senate, in 1997. During the George W. Bush Administration, healthcare reform advocates managed to pass the deficit-blowing Medicare Prescription Drug, Improvement and Modernization Act in 2003.

Reading between the lines, it seems eminently clear that healthcare reform was an unstoppable train, a juggernaut. If even George W. Bush was singing their tune, it was time for the Control System to add rocket boosters once his term was up. It was time to bring back Hillary, who by now had now added the impressive credential of United States Senator from New York to her already-stunning resume.

Things didn't work out quite as smoothly for Hillary in 2008 as she might have hoped. Or maybe she was just fine with the outcome, since Obama did the heavy lifting on her healthcare plan and appointed her Secretary of State, thereby making her the all-but-inevitable choice as his successor.

Now that the Republicans won the White House in 2016, they will use the Obamacare law's waiver feature to allow the states to experiment with novel ideas such as denying health coverage to poor people whenever an excuse can be created. Hedge fund manager and made-for-TV Facebook villain Martin Shkreli, who became notorious for raising exorbitantly the price for the 62-year-old "lifesaving" drug Daraprim, could well become head of Carly Fiorina's or Marco Rubio's FDA. Donald Trump, is already making hay with populist remarks about price-gouging drug companies. Even under the wise and dynamic leadership of President Trump, drug companies could achieve windfall profits without public backlash of the kind that forced Shkreli to back down as precipitously as he rose to the depths of infamy. Trump could turn out to be, the corporate champion of the people and good for business.

Five

"I no longer believe in Modern Medicine. I believe that despite all the super technology and elite bedside manner...the greatest danger to your health is the doctor who practices Modern Medicine. I believe that Modern Medicine's treatments for disease are seldom effective, and that they're often more dangerous than the disease they're designed to treat. I believe more than 90% of Modern Medicine could disappear from the face of the earth --- doctors, hospitals, drugs and equipment --- and the effect on our health would be immediate and beneficial... Modern medicine can't survive without faith, because Modern medicine is neither an art nor a science. It's a religion."

— DR. ROBERT MENDELSOHN, M.D.

Readers will be now be aware that I regard Obamacare as largely a hugely expanded clone of Hillarycare, which in turn was basically a bloated version of Enthoven's managed competition scheme for Jimmy Carter. Basically, healthcare reform is designed to limit competition among insurance companies; regulate and control doctors; promote the allopathic drug-centric medical model that has been so detrimental to public health; create work for corporate lawyers; and plow windfall profits into the hands of the wealthy financiers at whose behest the "new" system was created and promoted. It does a lot of other things, too: some are good, some are not so good. The good things, such as the continuation of medical coverage for dependents up to age 26 and wider availability of women's health services, do not take up many of the 11,000 pages.

One of the worst aspects of healthcare reform has yet to be enacted. This is the national ID card system that helped cause the failure of Jimmy Carter's original healthcare reform proposal. Hillarycare included a similar scheme; Obamacare does not require any such program. It will be interesting to see what Trumpcare includes.

There are some great things about requiring people to carry around with them their health insurance cards, and linking those cards to a computer database can serve many worthy purposes, some of them not just tangentially related to patient health. If a person arrives unconscious at an emergency room after an accident, learning quickly that she is diabetic could have a strong favorable influence on her prognosis for recovery, given that some drugs that might be used to revive a healthy patient could kill her.

In recent years, there has been much discussion of embedded microchips, which involve injecting a small device containing ID and health information in a patient's arm or other part of the body. Companies are already selling similar system for dogs to customers who want to make sure that their pet can never get lost.

The trouble with the American government is that if you give them an inch, they'll take a mile. Edward Snowden revealed that the National Security Agency spies on foreign and domestic telephone conversations and electronic communications. The Patriot Act, ostensibly designed to make it easier to monitor and apprehend terrorists, morphed into an all-embracing Big Brother system reminiscent of Goring's secret information bureaus and Stalin's NKVD. German Chancellor Angela Merkel was outraged to discover that the Obama administration was listening to her private telephone calls; many Americans shared Merkel's sense of betrayal at Snowden's revelations.

Why did J. Edgar Hoover spy on other homosexuals? Why did the FBI keep track of Martin Luther King, Jr.'s affairs? Why did the IRS go after people on Nixon's Enemies List? Coming up with the right answer does not require a great deal of thought. The government compiles and uses private information in order to be able to anticipate, control and block the activities of persons of interest.

The introduction of a national ID card or implanted chip is more than just a wedge to a universal voter ID card system. The technology now apparently exists whereby a hacker might be able to program a pacemaker to detonate. A demonstration test of this technology was called off recently due to the sudden premature death of one of the hackers who had bragged of being able to perform this feat.

Once the U.S. government has access to your identity; your GPS position; your entire medical and financial transaction history; all of your telephone calls and private communications; it is but a small step to that information getting hacked by Russian, Chinese, North Korean and ISIS computer and social media geeks.

Even our own government is capable of taking lethal action against or blackmailing American citizens. Drones make it even easier and more tempting than ever before. And don't think you can't become a drone target just because you are innocent: American Presidents have ordered the annihilation of Hiroshima and Nagasaki; the launch of the Vietnam war over a fabricated "incident" in the Gulf of Tonkin; and the Iraq War, which was based on false and forged information about Saddam Hussein's capabilities and intentions. If you are a conspiracy theorist or a person skeptical of the government's good faith, you may also believe that elements in the U.S. government conspired to carry out and cover up the assassination of President John F. Kennedy.

When the minions of David Rockefeller know everything about you from the contents of your colon to the password to your Wi-Fi network, we can no longer sustain the illusion that we are living in a free country. Mysterious deaths like Vincent Foster's or Anna Politkovskaya's may become the rule rather than the exception. Rationed care and price controls may be the least of our worries with Donald Trump in charge of administering Obamacare.

One of my own pet peeves about Obamacare is the danger that this kind of bureaucratic approach to healthcare reform poses to practitioners of alternative medicine. I worry that by driving sick people to the drug purveyors and the nuclear medicine experts as a matter of course, the government is causing harm to the very people who most need help. Healthcare choice is important, as is patient self-education about health and wellness. Turning over all our healthcare decisions to government bureaucrats and to doctors who are ordered to perform their functions according to mandates established in 11,000 pages of legal fine print is a recipe for trouble. We deserve better.

Six

The Triad of Power and Control

"There will be, in the next generation or so, a pharmacological method of making people love their servitude, and producing a kind of painless concentration camp of entire societies, so that people will in fact have their liberties taken away from them, but will rather enjoy it, because they will be distracted from any desire to rebel by propaganda or brainwashing, or brainwashing enhanced by pharmacological methods. And this seems to be the final revolution."

— Aldous Huxley

Two of the most powerful emotions on the planet are fear and love. They alone, can make you do things that your rational mind would never consider. Since this book focuses on health and wellbeing, I want to include guilt as an emotion in the equation.

The allopathic medical matrix in America understands and thrives on the fact that it is "emotion" that drives a person's actions, NOT reason. As a result, they have mastered the art of manipulating an individuals' emotional state, to get them to comply with their recommendations. This secures the mass social indoctrination process and conditions people to automatically distrust their own bodies ability to function, heal and adapt within the boundaries of Natural Law and the perfect cosmic arrangement of the Universe. These actions reinforce the public's continued dependence upon the allopathic medical model for its' illusion of health, all while keeping them submissive and continue to worship the medical physician at the altar of the white coat.

Fear, guilt and love are emotions that resonate so powerfully within the human body. Once activated and running at a high level of intensity, they have the ability to override any normal, logical and cognitive thought process within the brain. As a result, one's ability to use common sense, logic and reason becomes neutralized almost immediately. When this occurs, a person tends to react with an intense emotional response to a particular situation which he/she views as a negative one. While in this highly charged and emotional state, the power and control mechanisms of that individual are surrendered unconsciously and shifted to someone or something else. The power of that individual now becomes the control mechanism of the person or institution that created the intense emotional situation in the first place.

If a person is filled with enough fear, guilt or love in their heart, they can be controlled to do almost anything. The allopathic medical matrix in America uses fear and guilt as its driving force by way of the products and services it sells to its customers (i.e. toxic chemical drugs and surgery). The hidden hand of power that controls the medical matrix absolutely understands that the human body, because of its design, is compelled to obey Natural Law, not poison or destroy it. Therefore, a person who clearly understands what I have just described should never subject themselves, their children or loved ones to the methodologies of toxic chemical drug use or radical surgeries as a means of obtaining a state of health. These methodologies directly offend the principles of Natural Law and in no way produce or support health and wellbeing within the body. Those who understand this also understand the proper place for the allopathic medical model in society is to be used for "acute trauma care" only; very different than supporting and promoting health and wellness within the body and should never be confused.

For too long the American public has been talked down to, scolded and disrespected by allopathic medical doctors. Medical doctors are trained in medical school to place fear and guilt in the hearts of their patients by saying to those who were conditioned to blindly trust them, *"If you don't take this drug....this may happen...or that. You don't want it to spread do you? You need this surgery or you may die, have a stroke, heart attack or lose this body part"* Or, *"Your baby needs this...or that. If you don't do this to your baby it will put he/she at risk, and won't be protected. You don't want that to happen do you?"* You see, conformity gives control, fear and guilt give consent and emotions cloud judgment. Who is really the boss of you? The only correct answer is YOU!

Those of you that have children, I'm sure at some point your child has yelled at you this powerful statement, *"You're not the boss of me!"* If not, they most likely will at some point because children are innately imprinted with the will to explore and expand their individuality, not to conform. Conforming goes against human nature. I remember clearly, when both of my boys made this statement to my wife and I on more than one occasion. I still laugh about it.

It begs me to ask, what happened to us when we became adults? Where did that independent will of childhood go? What happened to the individual thinker who made sure that his or her parents understood their intent, will and power when the phrase *"You're not the boss of me!"* was screamed from across the room?

Unfortunately, in America today social conformity standards have evolved to such an extent that they have been specifically designed to purposefully condition the innate *"Will to Power"* (as Friedrich Nietzsche stated) out of the individual. The most criminal aspect of this social indoctrination process is that it occurs from birth and continuously evolves throughout a person's lifetime without them realizing it. They become hidden and accepted as "Social Norms" and if you don't conform, the backlash comes from your peers, not from the institution that instilled them within. How messed up is that?

This ability to manipulate physical, chemical and mental stimuli creates a "Master and Slave" relationship between the person experiencing the altered emotional state and the person or entity that both facilitates and creates them within the person's mind. The statement, *"Perception is reality"* holds much truth; just as a glass that is half empty is also half full. The only difference is how you are conditioned to see it. In reality, both are right, but how people see it is completely different and totally independent. Not surrendering to your emotions when being pressed with fear or guilt during any health crisis is the key to maintaining and securing your personal power and personal control over your life, health and wellbeing. Remember, *"No one is the boss of you!"*

I'd like to give the following example of how your emotions can be weaponized and used to control you. I would guess many people have experienced this type of scenario during their childhood, I sure did.

In the school yard, when a bully laughs at you, embarrasses you in front of your friends and then proceeds to call you names that you don't like, what do you do? If you choose to react intensely, get all upset and start cursing at him or her louder than he or she did at you, what normally happens? In most cases, the bully responds by continuing to laugh at you, then calls you even more names and teases you worse than when he or she started.

Looking at this situation from the out-side-in and with a clear rational mind, who would you say controls who? The answer is clear. In this emotionally charged situation, the bully always controls the person being bullied. Why? Because the person being bullied gives the bully exactly what he or she wanted; complete power and control.

Now if you took the same bully situation and chose to ignore them, what normally happens? In most cases they eventually stop. Why? Because you chose not to engage them and surrender your emotional state. As a result, your personal power remains solid and steadfast with you and not transferred to the bully instigating the situation. Understanding your emotions can and do, override your mind's ability to process and react to a certain situation properly, enables you to once again become and remain the "Boss of You." This is what true personal power looks and where it should remain throughout the course of your life; within you. Teach this to your children as well and they will be sure to thank you and love you for it.

Seven

A HEALTHCARE CONSULTATION WITH
YOUR MEDICAL DOCTOR

*"Sometimes people don't want to hear the truth because
they don't want their illusions destroyed."*

— *FRIEDRICH NIETZSCHE*

*"We cannot teach people anything; we can only
help them discover it within themselves."*

— *GALILEO GALILEI*

I have clearly defined a new definition of *health* as "the *expression* of the body's ability to appropriately adapt to physical, chemical and mental stimuli." I have also clarified a new definition of *wellness* as, "The body's *ability* to adapt to its internal and external environment accordingly." Together, both Health and Wellness (as defined above) equate to what I have coined as, *The Adaptability Factor.*

It is important to understand these two specific and very different definitions because what you have been programmed to believe is that if you do not have any symptoms, then you must be "healthy" and if you do have any type of symptoms then you must be "sick." This is simply not the case.

Symptoms are nothing more than "signs" that your body's *Adaptability Factor* is in action at the highest degree; a display that your body is aggressively responding to its environment on either a physical, chemical or mental level. These responses are always generated from the "inside-out" via both your Immune System and your Central Nervous System (CNS).

The Allopathic Medical Model would like you to believe that health can only be achieved via an "outside-in" process that always requires some type of artificial, chemical or surgical intervention. They completely understand how the body works from an anatomical and physiological basis, but their philosophical dogma indoctrinates the allopathic medical doctors to distrust the natural functions and adaptability potential of the human body. As a result, they blindly push drugs and surgeries as the only true paths towards health and wellness. You need to clearly understand that this is not possible.

According to the United States Food and Drug Administration (the FDA), which is a federal government agency, "Only a DRUG can treat, prevent or cure a disease." A drug is an artificial chemical that has been patented to be used in patients with specific disease processes. These drugs (so-called medicines) must also be "clinically tested" and within these clinical trials must be proven to be safe and effective. Safe and effective? Not quite sure how they define those terms considering all drugs are toxic to the body and each have some type of side-effect (which is really an effect). Drugs are created to simply manage a patient's symptoms, NOT to cure the disease. Curing disease directly affects the bottom line of the drug companies because they lose a customer. The *cause* of a person's disease, as well as *why* their body is no longer capable of properly adapting, is completely ignored within The Allopathic Medical Model and The Drug Trust. They are both in the business of simply managing symptoms and passing that management off as healthcare to the American public.

Since all drugs are artificial chemicals designed to be taken into the body, they are all toxic to varying degrees. They all produce a negative effect on the body's natural biochemical balance; as a result of their immediate toxicity and biochemical imbalance, the body's innate *Adaptability Factor* becomes triggered and goes into full effect as a protective response. The body's Adaptability Factor is set in motion to respond immediately via its immune system.

Since all drugs (in any amount) are toxic to our natural balanced biochemistry, they immediately attack the immune system and the body responds with an adaptability reaction to guard and protect itself. The degree to which the immune system can properly adapt to the introduction of any toxin is controlled and coordinated by the functional capacity of the person's central nervous system.

If one's body can adjust accordingly because their *Adaptability Factor* is high, then the drugs will be eliminated from the body within a timely manner. If not, the toxins will remain; becoming trapped and stored within the bodies tissues, causing potential long-term negative, physical, chemical and mental effects. How these negative effects manifest within the physical body over time is completely dependent upon whether the individual's *Adaptability Factor* is high or low. The higher a person's *Adaptability Factor*, the faster their body will return to a balanced biochemical state.

The manifestation of either health or wellness through the use of any type of artificial chemical drugs is not possible. As I mentioned earlier, the Allopathic Medical Monopoly and The Drug Trust was NOT designed to and is NOT interested in curing any type of disease; it is only interested in managing symptoms and making money at the expense of the patient's pain and suffering. This is why they use the term "treatment" and NEVER the word "cure."

Did you ever wonder why a person is always labeled a "cancer survivor," and never said to be "cured of cancer." Their motivation from the start has been, and always will be, is money, power and control, NOT the creation of health and wellness in any form. There is no money to me made in a society of healthy people. The Allopathic Medical Monopoly and The Drug Trust create customers, not cures!

Since the FDA informs the American people that "only drugs" can treat, prevent or cure disease, let us now use a little common sense and logic, as we explore the following allopathic medical doctor and patient "health consultation" interaction scenario.

A patient comes into his/her allopathic medical doctor's office for a health consultation and says to him or her, *"Doctor, I want to be as healthy and as vital as I can be. My health is the most important thing in my life right now. I understand that according to the FDA only a drug can treat, prevent or cure any disease. I was always taught that if I wanted to be my healthiest, that it would be wisest to do exactly what the health experts do themselves. I was told you are the health expert because you went to medical school and you teach and promote to your patients that drugs and surgery are the keys to health, I am here to talk to you because I want to know exactly what it takes to be healthy according to your medical training and knowledge. I'd like to ask you the following questions; Doctor, what drugs are you currently taking (specifically what brands and for what reason) and which types of surgeries have you had? I simply ask these questions because I want to be healthy too. You promote so strongly and confidently that the various drugs I see on TV are the keys to health that I must ask you personally, what drugs are you currently taking (exactly) to stay healthy because*

I want to start taking them too? The drug ads I see on TV get so confusing because I see so many of them these days; I just want to keep things as simple as possible. All I want for myself and my family is to be as healthy and vital as you are. So, please help me understand. Which drugs should I begin taking first and which surgical procedures should I schedule within the very near future?"

Wow...what a health consultation? Next, you need to ask yourself, *"If I don't want drugs and I don't want surgery, what other product or service is an allopathic medical doctor trained to provide me?"* The obvious answer is, *"Not much else."*

I find it very interesting that the current average lifespan of an allopathic medical doctor within the United States is only 57; so much for being a health and longevity expert? *"Do as I say, NOT as I do"* seems to be the universal statement of the allopathic medical doctor. As crazy and funny as the above consultation scenario sounds, if taking drugs and having surgeries really produced health, then we would be having these types of conversations with our medical doctors every day and the result would speak for itself. If the results were solid and proven, then the allopathic medical model would have created one of the healthiest, happiest and most vital nations on the planet; but it hasn't, its created one of the sickest. What truth does that tell you about their methodologies? It tells me is, they are severely flawed and need to be replaced immediately.

Final food for thought, *"If drugs were truly the key to good health and wellness, then shouldn't the people on the most drugs be the healthiest?"* The fact that they are the sickest, should speak to you more loudly than any of the brain washing drug ads on TV and radio do.

The only way for you to truly maximize your *Adaptability Factor* and become your healthiest is to learn to "Nurture Nature." You must begin to support and trust your body's natural, innate processes. You must also begin to obey the natural laws of creation and avoid all artificial, toxic nonsense of the allopathic medical system designed to keep you sick and enslaved. Allopathic medical care has its place; it's to provide "acute trauma care" to the American people. This is very different than healthcare and should not be confused as such if your goal is to get away from the *Generation SICK* model.

Eight

"I was not even aware of getting dressed, which was no simple matter: trousers and shirt, felt boots, over my shirt a leather jerkin, then an overcoat topped by a sheepskin, fur hat, and my bag containing caffeine, camphor, morphine, adrenalin, clamps, sterile dressings, hypodermic, probe, a Browning automatic, cigarettes, matches, watch, stethoscope."

— **MIKHAIL BULGAKOV,** *A COUNTRY DOCTOR'S NOTEBOOK*

Before fee-for-service medicine replaced the informal system of house calls and barter deals involving chickens and blueberry pies, long before medicine became just another branch of big business, the doctor/patient relationship was a central one in the lives of many people. One doctor may have delivered the babies and treated the children of a whole town's families for 40 or 50 years before being replaced by his son.

The modern medical system tends to destroy the doctor/patient relationship in many ways that ultimately can have unfortunate consequences for a patient's health and well-being. When a patient steps into a doctor's office today, she may be asked to sign a waiting list or even to take a number. Rarely do appointment times mean anything. Every internal medicine doctor's office is a poorly-equipped Emergency Room. Doctors are pressed for time, and a patient who has been waiting for hours may get as little as a minute or two to discuss her symptoms. Such interactions are not conducive to gaining a proper appreciation of the factors that may be making a person sick.

The great Russian writers Chekhov and Bulgakov were trained as doctors before becoming literary men. When we read some of their short stories based on their experiences as doctors, we get the sense that the compassion and the sense of shared danger they felt when treating their patients gave them the ability to convey the essence of the human experience better than almost anybody before or since.

In the old days, a doctor was involved in the community. Everywhere he walked, he attracted the adoring glances of neighbors he had cured of syphilis, swimmer's ear, rheumatism or some other disease. When he appeared at the funerals of his patients, he gave the family a greater sense of solace than the town priest or rabbi. A doctor was someone who understood people, someone who cared about people; and people loved him back.

Today, things are a little different. Now that the lawyers and businessmen have got their claws into everything, the love on both sides of a medical transaction is tempered by a sense that both parties are engaging in a business meeting. In the Norman Rockwell era, visiting the doctor was a personal occasion, just as cherished as a night of lovemaking with a spouse or lover. Those days are gone forever. The modern medical consultation has all the charm of a visit with a prostitute or a gigolo. There is no casual conversation and no kissing, just a lot of washing up and a lot of money being passed across the counter. While many patients walk out at the end with a satisfied smile and a feeling of relief, it is an increasingly rare event that a patient gets the feeling that the doctor cares about him or her personally. The feeling goes double for the doctor. Insurance company reimbursements barely cover the cost of maintaining a water cooler and magazines in the waiting room. If a doctor can't find a way to keep the stream of patients steady and the consultations short, he will quickly be forced out of the medical profession and might end up instead as an Uber driver or a salesman for a pharma company.

Each patient a doctor sees is a potential lawsuit, so doctors are careful to order batteries of tests whenever possible and to call in a specialist for all doubtful cases. Besides the overhead for diagnostic equipment and supplies; office and cleaning staff; rent; continuing education and whatever else is required by law and custom to equip a medical office, today's doctor has to set aside a hefty chunk of cash to cover malpractice insurance, an absolute must in our litigious society. If current trends continue, doctors and patients may meet nearly as often in the courtroom as in the consulting room.

Robert McNamara, Enthoven's boss at the U.S. Defense Department, entered the government from Ford Motor Company, where he had learned to deal effectively with assembly lines, logistics, procurement, personnel management and other industrial engineering matters. McNamara brought his industrial business management skills to the Defense Department. Budgets ballooned as the Vietnam War ramped up. Among the legacies McNamara left, aside from the war that he later confessed had been a terrible mistake, was a weapons production system that suffered chronic problems with cost overruns. By the time investigators took a look under the hood, the government was famously caught paying as much as $50 for a single screw or other trivial item that could have been purchased at a corner hardware store for a dime or a quarter; or $100 for a hammer. Because of cronyism, preferential contracts, corruption, wasteful practices and other habits that always seem to be part of the cost of doing business for the United States government, we managed to put the brakes on what had been a roaring economy while still losing the war. The war was not the only program sucking life from the economy, of course: the Great Society programs such as Medicare and the War on Poverty also had a considerable impact, but at least those programs were good for getting votes.

McNamara set great store on knowing what could be known about the enemy: he set up the Defense Intelligence Agency as an autonomous entity. His efforts to penetrate the fog of war were mostly in vain, however. George Carlin's list of oxymorons included "military intelligence." Carlin may have come up with this terse remark after reflecting on the conduct of McNamara's spies and generals, who constantly inflated the body count of enemy dead to make it seem to their civilian paymasters as if victory were just around the corner.

David Halberstam dubbed McNamara and his "Whiz Kids" such as Enthoven "the best and the brightest." Some of these geniuses who came up with our losing Vietnam War strategy also had an honored place at the table in the decades-long series of Jackson Hole healthcare reform planning meetings. It should come as no surprise that many of the same issues arose in connection with Obamacare and its predecessor schemes as had bedeviled us in Southeast Asia: cost overruns; bureaucratic incompetence; plausible deniability; camouflage. Substitute "death panels" for "body bags," and you have almost a complete DNA match!

Back in the Fifties, Eisenhower supporters wore campaign buttons saying, "I Like Ike." When asked to name an admirable personal trait of

Hillary's during a primary debate, Barack Obama came up with a similar formula: "You're likeable enough, Hillary."

Obama may have put his finger on an important point: while her husband Bill was a loveable rogue admired by millions, Hillary Clinton was at best a "likeable enough" interlocutor in a negotiation or business meeting. She has lived her life in Bill's big shadow, and has had a hard time trying to stand on her own two feet since the moment she first caught the nation's attention. This lack of public appeal may have led to her Presidential loss to Donald Trump in 2016?

In 1993, Hillary's healthcare plan flopped. It was an embarrassing failure on the national stage. Most Americans felt that she had flubbed her cue. No sane pundit would have predicted that she could ever emerge from that disaster to become a plausible Presidential candidate within just 15 years.

All Presidential candidates ask the public for love and devotion to their programs and to their persons. Politics is intoxicating and addictive. Losing a political battle leaves deep scars, but once you have the bug, you can never stop until you reach the top or die trying. Perennial losers like Harold Stassen and Mitt Romney and Hillary Clinton and Rick Santorum are like the radioactive cockroaches that survived the human race in "The Day After," a TV drama about the effects of nuclear war. They just keep coming.

No matter how unpopular her program was in 1993, Hillary Clinton has remained determined to stick with healthcare reform as her meal ticket and calling card; and in the process of persuading people to adopt her ideas, she hopes to gain respect, admiration and yes, love.

The American people have spoken and in 2016 elected Donald Trump as the next President of the United States. As the first self-proclaimed "non-politician" elected President, I sincerely hope his time in office will represent a historic period of peace and prosperity for the country. I just believe that Obamacare is a loser for the American people, and I worry that if he can't get healthcare right, he'll probably mess up everything else.

I hope that Trump's experience with the inevitable hiccups and failures of Obamacare implementation will encourage him to think more deeply about the real healthcare needs of the American people. It took Nixon to break the ice with China; maybe Trump will be the one to break the chains inherent in the managed competition scheme. There is a precedent, after all. Rockefeller and J.P. Morgan thought they had Theodore Roosevelt in their pockets, and look how that turned out for them. Their stooge ended up being a trustbuster, and soon Standard Oil was no more!

If Donald Trump manages to get a copy of this book and absorbs its lessons, perhaps there is a chance that the lumbering ship of state will reverse course and head to a saner, healthier future. When I see that process begin to build steam, I will gladly go on Trump2020.com to purchase a "Making America Great Again!" campaign button.

Nine

*"As I see it, the wise thing for the medical profession to do, is
to get right into and man every great health movement; man
health departments, tuberculosis societies, child and infant welfare
societies, housing societies, etc. The future of the profession
depends on keeping matters so that when the public mind thinks
of these things it automatically thinks of physicians, and not of
sociologists or sanitary engineers. The profession cannot afford
to have these places occupied by other than medical men."*

— **DR. W.A. EVANS,** ONE-TIME HEALTH
COMMISSIONER FOR THE CITY OF CHICAGO AT THE
ANNUAL CONVENTION OF THE AMA, 1911.

In February 1992, President George H.W. Bush tried to seize the high
ground on healthcare reform by proposing a "managed competition"
healthcare plan based largely on the work of Stanford professor Alain
Enthoven. Bill Clinton, who initially had favored a system of price controls as a way to make healthcare and insurance more affordable, found

himself attacked as a Big Government socialist. In order to blunt these attacks, Clinton adopted the Republican plan as his campaign platform.

Once in office, Clinton put his wife in charge of making sense of Bush's plan. Hillary Clinton and her team of wonks consulted secretly with the leading healthcare reform minds of the time, the Jackson Hole crowd and major insurance company lobbyists, and came up with 1,342 pages that pleased almost no one, and that nearly killed her husband's administration and her career to boot.

In 1993, Daniel Patrick Moynihan, who would eventually be Hillary Clinton's predecessor and sponsor at the U.S. Senate, criticized the part of Hillarycare that proposed limiting costs by cutting the number of doctors by 25% and the number of specialists in half: "If you have fewer doctors you have fewer doctor bills, but you don't associate it with improving medicine." (Unless, of course, your chief advisors on healthcare are the AMA and the Rockefellers.)

Enthoven, whose "managed competition" plan for Jimmy Carter had eventually morphed, first into Hillarycare, then into Obamacare, hated many of the concrete legislative proposals that his plan inspired over the following decades. The man who starting the ball rolling on healthcare reform wrote in 1993 that Hillarycare "threatens to be a monopolistic, regulatory government agency that will cause more problems than it solves… The first thing Congress should do is delete pages 1 through 1,342 of Clinton's 1,342-page bill."

Not all healthcare reforms met with Enthoven's disapproval. Enthoven enthusiastically endorsed President George W. Bush's prescription drug plan, which does not allow the government to negotiate drug prices, because drugs are frequently sold by monopolists who need big profits in order to finance continued research and development. Enthoven, ever the realist, appreciated Bush's understanding that it was useless for the government to negotiate with a monopolist, who could simply refuse to sell life-saving drugs such as Viagra (Pfizer's perennial top seller) if the price were set too low.

Bush's education on the importance of drug industry testing and innovation was undoubtedly accelerated by the fact that his campaigns for President were among the largest beneficiaries of the multi-billion-dollar pharmaceutical and health industry products lobby.

Needless to say, given the scale of the drug industry largesse to promising politicians, the hugely expensive Medicare Prescription Drug Plan was one of the very few aspects of President Bush's legacy that Obama did not seek to reverse upon taking office. Although not technically part of the ACA, the Bush Medicare Prescription Drug Plan is now enshrined as a central plank of the complex of healthcare laws and regulations we now generically call Obamacare.

Obamacare was never inevitable, just all-but-inevitable. Many liberal Democrats supported a single-payer system for healthcare, under the theory that healthcare is a right, not just a business, and the medical establishment should therefore not be run as if it were just another profit center for large corporations. The right goal for these Democrats was to create a national health service on the European model. Unfortunately, such a model could not clear the Congress, where many regarded such a "socialized medicine" scheme as an attack on the American way of life. Plan B was Romneycare, which Obama adopted.

Alain Enthoven should have been a happy camper, but he was not thrilled with Obamacare in its final form. After years of trying to convince policymakers that "managed competition" was the key to save money on healthcare costs, Enthoven had come to recognize that healthcare reform was doomed to failure: "One of the most important lessons that has come out of the current "reform" process is the enormous power of the medical industrial complex and their large financial contributions and armies of lobbyists to block any significant cost containment."

The trouble with Obamacare, according to Enthoven, is that "the American people are being deceived" because the Affordable Care Act does "little or nothing to curb the expenditures." Enthoven felt that, since the Obama approach did not do enough to control healthcare spending, the eventual result of enacting the ACA would be higher interest rates and an increase in the budget deficit.

Enthoven recognized that the opposition party was even worse than the Democrats: "Our anguish is only intensified by the fact that the Republicans are no better at fiscal responsibility, probably worse as they demagogue reasonable attempts to limit expenditures." Perhaps the best-known example proving Enthoven's point is Sarah Palin's fear-mongering rhetoric over "death panels" that would promote euthanasia by denying advanced medical treatment to the very old.

Enthoven's plan in its various incarnations was never a simple matter of people before profits. The idea of limiting competition was geared toward advantaging existing healthcare conglomerates and drug monopolies in order to cut costs associated with competition. Enthoven thought it would be possible to cover more people by leveraging system resources to reduce expenses. His thoughts on these matters were greatly prized by the insurance companies and philanthropic foundations that funded his studies over the years.

Healthcare as a business is an odd duck. There are many diseases that are easily treated or can go away on their own. Other diseases, such as cancer, are hard to detect and even harder to treat. Advanced treatments can generate huge profits based on a captive audience of desperate people willing to throw their money down a rat hole based on a very remote chance of recovery. Putting all these factors together into a "one-size-fits-all" national system is a daunting challenge.

Five years after its passage, the Affordable Care Act seems to be doing pretty well, especially considering the acrimony that attended its passage, the software glitches that marred its launch, and the dire predictions made by its detractors. The law has now passed two Supreme Court tests; and an alternative Republican healthcare reform plan is no closer to formulation than it was in 2010. Indeed, as we have seen, Obamacare *is* the Republican alternative to the fully government-run national health insurance system that leading liberal experts would prefer. While its basis is Enthoven's work for Jimmy Carter, many of the key Obamacare ideas came from the Heritage Foundation, and from the two Bush administrations.

We are now seeing what appear to be impressive results from Obamacare reforms. Millions more people have access to insurance, and most of the new subsidized customers are very pleased with their new coverage. The Republicans continue to vote for repeal, but most observers recognize that Obamacare is here to stay. In fact, perhaps the biggest beneficiary of the Supreme Court decisions was the clown car of Republican Presidential candidates, who now no longer have to worry about millions of Red State citizens being thrown off their insurance plans.

The Congressional Budget Office recently published a study stating that repealing Obamacare would likely add hundreds of billions of dollars to the Federal deficit, meaning that Republicans would need to replace Obamacare with a massive tax increase in order to keep pace with our debts. Starving the beast by closing down the Federal government over Obamacare is a strategy that has already been tried and found wanting. That means we are in for more of the same with a Donald Trump Presidency.

Any objective look at the history and contents of Obamacare would have to conclude that both political parties are responsible for leading us to where we are on healthcare reform, probably because politicians of all persuasions have been successfully co-opted by the Drug Lobby. The future answer to any perceived problem with the medical delivery system will undoubtedly be doubling down with more of the same: increase the barriers to entry for the medical profession; protect drug company and insurance company profits at all costs; weed out alternative healthcare providers; keep people in the dark about the actual financial and social costs of their healthcare system.

The Rockefeller name is widely associated with the War on Drugs, under which New York State cracked down on the narcotic and psychedelic drugs Nelson Rockefeller blamed for an epidemic of crime in the Sixties. It turned out years later that the real culprit for the crime wave, at least according to the widely influential bestseller *Freakonomics,* was the lack of access to safe, affordable abortion during the generation prior to the turbulent Sixties. Once lower-class ladies such as prostitutes and the girlfriends of juvenile delinquents were able to choose abortion, Mayor Giuliani was able to reap the benefits as that last cohort of Baby Boomers came of age, with notably fewer unwanted babies in their ranks. Murder rates dropped precipitously as a consequence of high abortion rates among the lower classes in New York during the age of Vietnam, the pill, and rock and roll.

Nelson Rockefeller's crime-fighting strategy, which he copied from Japan's "zero tolerance" policy, centered on long-term incarceration for hippies and other low-life dirt bags caught with pot, cocaine, heroin, LSD or crystal meth. The United States now has more people – over two million – behind bars than any other country. A lot of people used drugs and committed crimes in New York State, but most of the people arrested and sent to prison under Rockefeller's drug laws were poor blacks and Hispanics. Rockefeller's tough approach was copied by other states, including California, which passed mandatory sentencing and three-strikes laws.

I have always believed that the Rockefeller Drug Laws were just another element of the Rockefeller family's longstanding attempt to control the medical establishment, partly by cornering the market on prescription and over-the-counter drugs. Narcotics, which were peddled by organized crime, inner-city gangs, and international smugglers, represented a black market alternative form of ingestible and injectable chemical cocktails from which the Rockefeller family received no revenue. Putting drug dealers in prison killed two birds with one stone: you not only eliminated a cohort of unwanted competitors, but also obtained a large group of guinea pigs on whom you could test the latest pharmaceutical treatments for drug addiction withdrawal and other conditions unrelated to drug abuse.

Drugs have become an indispensable element of life and death in prison, as increasingly outside of prison. Along with the VA system and the Medicare bureaucracy, prison healthcare is now one of the government's big medical monopolies. States spend roughly $8 billion each year on healthcare for prisoners. As the median age of prisoners rises, more and more prisoners require cancer treatment, dialysis, and other expensive procedures associated with end of life care.

America's prisons are a fertile ground for medical experiments and drug testing, as indicated by numerous leaks from whistle-blowing guards and unwilling test subjects written into the public record by intrepid journalists. Anyone who has ever visited a prison commissary can easily see that the murderers and rapists serving her lunch are heavily medicated with sedatives.

While it has been widely known for centuries that a gunshot to the head is an effective means of terminating a person's life, most prisoners facing execution by the state in the United States today are treated to a cocktail of drug injections that sedate, paralyze and finally kill. This "murder by injection" image was used by independent researcher Eustace Mullins as the title of his 1988 book on the American healthcare system; and as a metaphor for the large and growing problem of the poisoning of our bodies and our environment by over-reliance on powerful drugs, dangerous cancer treatments, and chemical fertilizers.

Mullins, never met a conspiracy theory he didn't fully embrace, maintained that Pearl Harbor and 9/11, and everything evil thing that happened in between, were inside jobs. He condemned George Bush's New World Order in vitriolic terms. Mullins had learned much of his routine from Ezra Pound, one of the Twentieth Century's greatest modernist poets, whom he visited at St. Elizabeth's Hospital for the Mentally Ill once a week during the early Fifties. Pound never acknowledged losing his marbles, but regarded himself as a political prisoner. Mullins credits Pound for putting him on the path that would lead him to uncover the secrets of the Federal Reserve in the stacks of the Library of Congress.

It is easy to dismiss Mullins as a crank, but it would be a mistake to underestimate his influence on American conservatives and libertarians. In recent years, Ron Paul and his son Rand Paul, are leading proponents of Mullins' deeply negative views on the Federal Reserve System. Mullins' views on healthcare are even more negative, and arguably even more influential.

Mullins' critique of the American healthcare system, which focused on the role of John D. Rockefeller and his allies in promoting allopathic medicine as part of a scheme to corner the drug market worldwide, is harder to dismiss, because many of the allegations Mullins made are consistent not only with the historical record, but also with critiques made by numerous independent journalists and writers in the nearly two decades since *Murder by Injection* appeared. Mullins' inflammatory statements on FDA corruption; on profiteering and influence buying by drug companies; and on the health impacts of drugs with powerful side effects are widely echoed not only in works by far-out conspiracy theorists such as Robert Barefoot's *Disease Conspiracy and* Jim Marrs' *Trillion-Dollar Conspiracy;* but also in popular mainstream books including Fran Hawthorne's *Inside the FDA* and Alison Bass' *Side Effects,* which explores conflicts between government and academia, deceptive drug marketing, skewed drug trials and the misleading of doctors and healthcare consumers by one of the world's leading drug manufacturers.

Make no mistake: healthcare reform has become as much, if not more, about expanding the power of pharmaceutical conglomerates and large insurance companies than about providing symptom relief to the masses. Now that the drug companies have achieved more monopoly power than John D. Rockefeller could have imagined in his wildest wet dream, they need a period of calm to consolidate these gains. Now that Donald Trump is President, only time will tell how he will handle the current Rockefeller controlled Allopathic Medical Monopoly and The Drug Trust.

Ten

Monopoly Healthcare

"There will be, in the next generation or so, a pharmacological method of making people love their servitude, and producing dictatorship without tears, so to speak, producing a kind of painless concentration camp for entire societies, so that people will in fact have their liberties taken away from them, but will rather enjoy it, because they will be distracted from any desire to rebel by propaganda or brainwashing, or brainwashing enhanced by pharmacological methods. And this seems to be the final revolution."

— ALDOUS HUXLEY

When John D. Rockefeller signed on to Frederick Gates' plan to protect his family assets from taxation and expand his influence by philanthropic activities meant to transform the American educational and medical landscape, he was the richest man in the world and had perhaps a dozen peers, among them Andrew Carnegie, J.P. Morgan, and Henry Ford, who could compete or (mostly) collude with him to establish the patterns that would shape the world to come. Today, power is concentrated, relatively speaking, in even fewer hands, thanks in large measure to the vision implemented by the institutions these men and their confreres created and made possible, among them the Rockefeller Foundation, the Ford Foundation, the Council on Foreign Relations, the Carnegie Endowment, ExxonMobil, CVS, Walgreens and JPMorganChase.

Rockefeller Foundation talent scouts identified and promoted rising stars such as Hans Bethe, who would become head of the Theoretical Division at Los Alamos, and Henry Kissinger, America's greatest statesman, whose rise to power was funded by Rockefeller largesse. Kissinger worked from 1956-58 as Director of the Rockefeller Brothers Fund Special Project, which Nelson Rockefeller conceived as a means of identifying international challenges and opportunities and designing American foreign policy responses. Kissinger continued to advise Nelson Rockefeller until he was chosen by President Nixon as National Security Advisor, and served together with Rockefeller during the subsequent Ford Administration.

Another brilliant man who worked with Rockefeller and Kissinger on Special Projects was Edward Teller, father of the H-bomb, who later inspired Ronald Reagan's "Star Wars" program, which Mikhail Gorbachev credited with bankrupting the Soviet Union.

The Rockefeller family was also deeply involved in American's greatest fiascos. David Rockefeller, who had persuaded Jimmy Carter to name Paul Volcker as Fed Chairman, also persuaded Carter to admit the Shah of Iran to travel to the United States for medical treatment, an invitation that backfired when Iranian students seized the American embassy in Tehran.

Why did America's most influential family, which had access to the levers of power in so many areas of American life, make such a massive effort to achieve dominance over the American healthcare system, and why does the Control System they have established feel that Hillary Clinton is the ideal candidate to fly their banner for the next few years?

Let's start with the obvious. The wind beneath the sails of the Rockefeller fortune is oil. After Jimmy Carter responded to the oil price shock caused by the Iranian revolution of 1979 by encouraging production of higher-mileage cars and wearing sweaters on TV to prove the point that a lower thermostat setting was your patriotic duty as an American, "Mr. Malaise" quickly found himself on the losing end of the field. He was nearly defeated by Ted Kennedy in his battle for re-nomination, and he was walloped by Ronald Reagan in November. The same thing, more or less, happened in 2000. The Clinton Administration had signed on to the Kyoto Protocol, an agreement designed to combat the threat of global warming. The Democratic nominee in 2000, Al Gore, aka "The Ozone Man," was even more committed to environmental causes. The Powers That Be were not amused. Gore won a plurality of the popular vote, but his hopes for winning Florida and therefore the Presidency were crushed when Trilateral Commission member, CFR stalwart and former Treasury Secretary James Baker stepped in to lead a scorched earth campaign that delivered the White House to Texas oilman George W. Bush.

The Bush Administration – eight years long – provided a breathing period during which the large oil companies could build up their cash reserves by raising prices; by building up American energy independence with fracking and off-shore drilling; and by making strategic investments in other new energy technologies that will allow them to maintain their dominant position for years to come. The only monkey wrench was Bush's obsession with Iraq. As far as the oil interests were concerned, Bush's Middle East obsession violated the Prime Directive of business: "Don't shit where you eat." Bush and Cheney expected that new oil service contracts could be generated by domination of Iraq; they failed to anticipate the multi-trillion dollar losses and near-economic collapse that would be the Iraq War's chief legacies.

John McCain wanted to double down on Bush's Middle East war disasters. He proposed arming the Kurds, the Libyans, the Syrians, the Georgians, the Ukrainians and pretty much everyone else stirring up trouble in oil-rich regions. He also aimed his firepower at the large financial institutions, which he charged with profiteering and corruption. The "Straight Talk Express" was set on a bridge to nowhere when McCain chose former Wasilla beauty contest contestant Sarah Palin as his running mate. She got a cram course from Henry Kissinger on national security affairs, but the best she could manage in the Vice Presidential debates was a comment about being able to see Russia from her window. Tina Fey's spot-on parody of Palin's debate performance made her the toast of Rockefeller Center. Yes, Palin was toast and McCain's hopes went up in smoke.

Hillary Clinton, despite her fine pioneering work on healthcare back in the 1990s, had also voted in favor of the Iraq War. Obama, who had voted against it, was able to use that club to throw Hillary and John McCain both under the bus.

Hillary Clinton has now apologized for her great sin of voting for the Iraq War; and she has served competently as Secretary of State. In her latest incarnation, she has accumulated a large fortune and assumed a leadership position at her family philanthropic foundation, which has worked closely with other leading charitable trusts on special projects in energy, healthcare, empowerment of women, education and promotion of computer literacy around the world.

It is no secret that Rockefellers love computers. During IBM's heyday, holdings of IBM stock were second only to those of Standard Oil of California in the family's investment portfolio. JPMorganChase, which

David Rockefeller led for many years, is widely known in the banking industry for having the best IT system in the business. David Rockefeller himself was reputed to be the world's greatest master of the Rolodex. In his memoirs, he modestly claimed to have a contact list of more than 1,000 names. In urban legend, his "electronic Rolodex" consists of more than 100,000 entries.

The Rockefeller link with IBM goes deeper than a shared love of database systems. It has roots in a shared admiration of Germany that many today would say went much too far. The Rockefeller Foundation financed the eugenics research of Otmar Verschuer and his assistant Josef Mengele at the Kaiser Wilhelm Institute. At one point during the interwar years, I.G. Farben, the world's largest chemical company at the time, was the second-largest shareholder, after John D. Rockefeller, of Standard Oil stock.

Rockefeller's patent oil salesman father had thought of oil as a medical substance, and John D. Rockefeller had ambitions to create a drug cartel that would far outstrip the monopoly power he had gained thanks to the oil business. His reciprocal investment partnership with I.G. Farben was in line with that goal, and continued throughout the war.

I.G. Farben produced vaccines and drugs, as well as poison gases and rocket fuels, but its partnership with Standard Oil did not benefit only German doctors and medical patients. It was allegedly through I.G. Farben's 1938 intervention with Standard Oil that the Luftwaffe obtained from Standard Oil the 500 tons of tetraethyl lead needed to fuel operations against Poland the following year. I.G. Auschwitz, using know-how provided by Standard Oil experts, produced synthetic oil to fuel the German war machine at the same location where its poison gases were employed to kill four million in the service of Hitler's Final Solution.

Thomas G. Watson, Sr. was also involved in lucrative business deals with Germany during the Nazi years. According to Edwin Black's best-selling book *IBM and the Holocaust*, IBM's Hollerith punch card technology helped the Nazis identify Jews and organize the concentration camps where they were worked to death and killed.

Computers are even better than punch cards for keeping track of people. LinkedIn and Facebook and Twitter are the poster boys for the wonders of communication in the digital age, but the recent revelations of Edward Snowden, as well as the epidemic of hacking into department store, credit card and government databases, have shown us the dark side of the Age of Machines.

Bill Gates, piggybacking on IBM's development and promotion of mainframe computers to create the first user-friendly computer operating system, together with Steve Jobs, who with partner Steve Wozniac developed the first consumer-friendly personal computer, created the next stage of the Computer Revolution, which went into high gear when the Netscape Browser and AOL opened the wonders of the Internet to ordinary people in the United States and around the world.

During the Clinton Administration, the Internet frenzy morphed into the Dotcom boom and bust, where fortunes were won and lost. The American economic engine went into overdrive, achieving phenomenal levels of prosperity and growth. Bill Gates became the world's richest man, a title he holds even today; and Microsoft's biggest rival, Apple Computer, is now the world's largest company by market capitalization. One of the Dotcom companies, Google, Inc., founded in 1998, is now the world's leading search provider and provider of software for mobile phones. Another Dotcom company, Amazon.com, founded as Cadabra in 1994, is the leading online retailer.

Al Gore, who famously caught heat for suggesting that he was an inventor of the Internet, has now become a media mogul and full-fledged member of the Silicon Valley hierarchy. No way he is going back to politics. With Gore out, and Hillary Clinton losing the 2016 Presidential election, the clear choice to lead us to the next Dotcom revival is Donald Trump.

Technology is a two-edged sword. It can be used to free us, or it can be harnessed to control us. Along with the life-saving miracle treatments that generate all the positive press, there are millions of life-altering and life-destroying medical bills that bankrupt whole families and communities. A simple vaccination can generate a $500 bill. In a hospital setting, as at a defense plant, things that might cost a dollar at the corner store may generate charges of hundreds or even thousands of dollars on a hospital bill. A hospital charter or a medical degree is practically a license to print money, and the trends that created this situation are only accelerating.

Hospitals and other medical businesses today generate bills that are not only inflated, but even fraudulent in many cases. Doctors blame insurance companies and vice versa. Computer-generated bills for a simple life experience such as pregnancy may go on for pages of tiny print. Explanations of these charges are printed even smaller than the dollar amounts, and may include terms and acronyms that only an M.D./Ph.D. or a medical writer readily understands. While complaining to Eyewitness News may occasionally get you an apology or a partial refund, most people have little recourse other than to pay. Doctors and hospitals are closely allied with banks and credit agencies. Not paying a medical bill will impact your credit score, and therefore your ability to buy a house, get a job, or even to get the 5% cash-back payments that people have come to expect when shopping for groceries or buying gas.

A person who can submit a healthcare bill 1,342 pages long will be delighted to promulgate executive orders based on 11,000 pages that almost no one else in America will ever read. Donald Trump has shown that he is comfortable with complicated tax structures, public/private partnerships and automation of administrative functions.

Now that Donald Trump has been elected as the next President, a major theme of the next decade will be the increasing integration of IT with the healthcare and financial system. Medical bills and insurance payments will be auto-debited from your account once a diagnosis is made or a new mandate instituted. At the same time, medical decisions and medical care will increasingly be placed in the capable hands of robots and computer algorithms. IBM's Watson system will diagnose your illness; robot maids will clean your bedpan at the hospital; and high-tech dispensing machines will inject the required medicines into your bloodstream as required.

Automation is not unique to the healthcare field. Over the next few years, we may see Uber drivers replaced by Google cars; pilots replaced by auto-pilots; and jobs replaced by leisure, otherwise known as uncompensated unemployment. Keeping the statistics favorable so that the economy looks healthy may require manipulation of certain indicators so that things look less hopeless than they are and the Stars and Stripes banner can continue to wave proudly over housing project doorways every Memorial Day and Fourth of July.

A terrorist act by 19 Muslim fanatics bankrolled by an evil Saudi millionaire led to many things that otherwise would not have happened: the creation of the Homeland Security bureaucracy that fails to enforce border security; the launching of two wars that killed many times the number of people as the three suicide airplane attacks; and the passage of the Patriot

Act, which allowed the United States government to monitor communications among people worldwide.

Any person with a glancing knowledge of American history knows that once the government assumes a power or creates a new entitlement, there is no turning back. The IRS is here to stay, and taxes tend to rise with every fiscal year. Medicare, once derided as socialized medicine, is now, in tandem with Social Security, the bedrock of our way of life once we get older. Combining the power of the Patriot act spying apparatus with access to medical records in vast electronic databases would vastly increase the government's ability to monitor potential terrorists, and this would happen in a heartbeat if another national security threat appeared to make it a reasonable preventive measure.

What the government does with your financial records, your health records, your gun ownership and property records depends who is running the government. Even with Donald Trump as the President, much of the awesome power of the Presidency will be directed to tracking down simple pieces of paper such as the secret back entrance logs at the White House between 1993 and 2001. No harm done. An enquiring mind wants to know. Where we run into trouble is when one of her successors or out-of-control subordinates has the corrupt and paranoid mentality of a Richard Nixon or Lyndon Johnson. Maybe the Donald Trump version of Nixon's Enemies List has 100,000 names, and any one of us could be on it, meaning that a drone strike up the ass might not be so easy to avoid.

Donald Trump is the loud-mouth, egotistical face of the Control State. Given his characteristic alpha-male demeanor, it is virtually impossible to know whether he realizes to what degree the owners of this country are planning to use him as a willing tool to bring about the final victory of moneyed interests over the American people under the innocent guise of healthcare reform.

I wrote this book as a warning call to the American citizens, who may be too complacent about their supposed freedom and security from the ever-metastasizing tumor represented by monopoly capitalism and its version of healthcare reform.

Eleven

"Soylent green is people!"

— **CHARLTON HESTON** LINE FROM THE CLASSIC
1973 SCIENCE FICTION FILM SOYLENT GREEN

Thanks in large measure to John D. Rockefeller and his monopolistic colleagues Thomas Alva Edison and Henry Ford, we now live fully in a world created by men of means and scientific (or at least patent-acquiring) ingenuity rather than the world given to us by God and all the savages who came before us. Ours is a world of side effects, unintended consequences, and foreseeable disasters such as Climate Change, black hole collisions and plastic-rich sea beds. General Electric, the company J.P Morgan created from Edison's electric ideas, and Ford Motor, the company that brought us the Model T and Robert McNamara, were fully as complicit as Standard Oil and IBM in making Hitler's trains run on time and paving the way for his wars against his neighbors and against his own people (as Bush and Cheney used to say about Saddam Hussein and the Kurds he gassed).

It would be totally unfair to paint John D. Rockefeller or any of his fellow monopolists as pure evil. In any event, that hatchet job has already been done by Ida Tarbell and scores of other capable writers who followed her lead. I urge you to read her brilliant works if you want to understand the depths to which humanity can stoop in the pursuit of monopoly power. What I did want to do in this book is just to point out that a tiger can't change its stripes. The mere fact that Rockefeller changed his focus from Standard Oil to the Rockefeller Foundation does not mean that he was no longer driven by the profit motive in later life.

The profit motive has been roundly condemned by everyone from Jesus Christ to Karl Marx to Vladimir Lenin to Kim Jong-Un to Thomas Picketty to Pope Francis, but you can't have it both ways. If your standard is "the greatest good for the greatest number," it is hard to argue with the fact that capitalism has played a huge part making that utilitarian dream a reality. A Communist society would not have produced Frank Sinatra or the Beatles or Madonna or Michael Jackson or Beyoncé. On the other hand, those who tout "the virtue of selfishness" are going way too far. Adam Smith's "invisible hand" has brought us the Invisible Government; invisible gases that poison our air; and Ralph Ellison's *Invisible Man*.

Who but a Luddite could wish away the invention of planes, trains and automobiles? Who wants to go back to the days when our viewing choices were limited to the offerings of NBC and CBS? While there will always be a few who prefer to live off the land and write their letters with a quill pen, most of us acknowledge that technology is here to stay. However, even the most avid technophiles have to admit that many of the best offerings are increasingly hidden behind an ever-higher pay wall: online subscriptions; high water bills; pay-per-view sports; steep tolls for highways and bridges.

With freedom comes responsibility; and with free money comes even more responsibility. We expect the rich to give back to the community. Philanthropy is not all bad, even if it is true that wealthy people often prefer to give to institutions and causes that further or celebrate their personal good fortune. J.P. Morgan was the leading force behind the creation of the Metropolitan Museum; many of the Rembrandts you see on the Met's wall are from his personal collection. While Benjamin Franklin established the first public lending library in the United States, it was Andrew Carnegie, the U.S. Steel tycoon perhaps best known today for founding Carnegie Hall, who put together the plan and the money that created the New York Public Library branch systems and other local library networks around the country. Leland Stanford, who was one of the main investors behind the building of the Transcontinental Railroad, founded Stanford University, today one of the leading breeding grounds of the tech industry.

Charities run by religious groups are usually no less dominated by self-interest. Salvation Army beneficiaries have to sing for their supper; but as Henry IV noted, "Paris is worth a mass." Catholic Charities is often among the first groups on the scene after a hurricane, earthquake, flood or tornado. What does it matter if their relief camps feature a crucifix in every tent?

It matters a lot. The purpose of organized religion, like the purpose of organized government, is to exercise control over large numbers of people by taking charge of their minds, their bodies and their money. Marx called religion "the opium of the people." That remark, its dead-on accuracy notwithstanding, did more than anything else he ever said to kill the Communist movement, as it was difficult to recruit the devout peasants of Europe to a godless ideology.

Stalin, whose disdain for religion was no doubt exacerbated by the scathing criticism of Pius XI (dubbed "Hitler's Pope" by historian John Cornwall) in his anti-Communist encyclical *Divine Redemptoris*, responded at Yalta to Churchill's plea to consider the views of the Vatican regarding the disposition of post-war Eastern Europe with sarcasm: "How many divisions does the Pope have?" It turned out that the Catholic Church, led by Polish-born pontiff John Paul II, would play a very large role in mobilizing the collapse and dismemberment of the Evil Empire that had defeated Nazi Germany just a generation after Stalin's death. Priests may not go around carrying machine guns, but their lame paeans to the Virgin Mary and the transubstantiation of the Holy Spirit raise tons of money, a substantial portion of which goes into the coffers of the secretive Vatican Bank, and into mostly tax-free real estate investments that have made the Catholic Church the world's leading private landowner.

A few words from the Pope, whom Catholics are duty-bound to consider infallible in matters of faith and morals, can rejigger entire ecosystems and unleash uncontrollable forces that overwhelm society. Pope Paul VI's 1968 encyclical *Humanae Vitae*, with its devastating attacks on abortion and birth control, contributed far more to the doubling of the population since then than the hippie slogan, "Make Love, Not War." Latin America, the epicenter of Catholic belief, has suffered some of the worst problems related to the subsequent massive population explosion. The Amazon forest, often called "the lungs of the planet," has been drastically trimmed back in order to accommodate millions upon millions of desperately poor Brazilian children whose birth was an unwanted and unplanned tribute to the Church's respect for life.

While early Rockefeller Foundation social investment took the opposite tack, by sponsoring research into population control, family planning and eugenics, the Rockefeller influence on society is hard to categorize as pure evil, even for the most ardent advocates of the pro-life strategy of blockading clinics and assassinating abortionists. That is because John D. Rockefeller was an intensely religious man who co-opted the strategy and vocabulary of religion to create a system that would resonate with the average American. The Rockefeller family built their own churches and schools and hospitals; to all but the most discerning eye, these institutions are identical to the parallel institutions of the Catholic Church.

The Rockefeller business and philanthropic strategies, like those of the other monopolists of their era and of today, were so successful because the family and their advisors figured out how to use the power of public relations to co-opt the other leading institutions of society and drive national policy in a direction favorable to family interests. Foremost among their tools were powerful appeals to patriotism and religion.

The great monopolist warmongers were always mindful never to disrespect the country that gave them the opportunity to build their vast fortunes. Standard Oil, Ford, GE and IBM may have played a central role in building up the German war machine, but their combined contributions to the American war effort far outstripped any of the relatively nickel and dime investments they may have made in Nazi-era German industry. The German investments loom large only because a little money went very far in Weimar inflation Germany, and because the scientists the Rockefellers chose to fund included 1918 Nobel Prize laureate Fritz Haber, inventor of the eponymous Haber-Bosch process, which is an essential step in the production of fertilizers and modern explosives. Haber's work on chemical weapons arguably prolonged the Great War by three years, and Hitler's reliance on nitrogen-based explosives and on the notorious Zyklon B gas represent a terrible burden on Haber's posthumous reputation; but it is also worth bearing in mind that half the world's population today depends on the fertilizer process he invented for its food supply.

Even such Control System proxies as Robert McNamara and Alain Enthoven and Edward Teller are not incarnations of unalloyed evil, and it is wrong to caricature them as such. McNamara's policies in Vietnam may have resulted in the death of millions of people, at least 58,000 of them American soldiers, but his introduction of seat belts into American consumer cars has arguably saved a far greater number of human lives. Enthoven's "managed competition" system may be a disaster for most people caught in the wheels of its bureaucracy, but we have to give him credit for accurately diagnosing some of the pitfalls of Obamacare. Edward Teller did more to make Mutually Assured Destruction possible than nearly anyone else, but his Star Wars plan accelerated the demise of a Soviet system that did more to enslave people and destroy the environment than anything that the worst robber barons ever pulled off.

John D. Rockefeller, Jr., whose talent for losing money in business deals was nearly as great as his father's talent in making money, redeemed himself in his father's eyes when he defended management's tactics in a 1914 incident involving the murder of women and children over a labor dispute at a Rockefeller-owned mine. Following that terrible human tragedy, "Junior" redoubled his efforts to whitewash the Rockefeller reputation. Working hand-in-hand at first with Frederick T. Gates, Junior largely succeeded in achieving rehabilitation of the family name by taking over the strategic management of the Rockefeller Foundation, and making it known as a force for good.

The Rockefeller Foundation can rightly claim to have done more good for more people than any other organization of its kind. While its early support for eugenics programs and radical family planning initiatives involve moral calculations that many would say negated any positive impact from such ventures, fighting world hunger is a cause that Jesus Christ would embrace with his whole Sacred Heart. The Rockefeller Foundation was a leading source of funding for the Green Revolution, a technology transfer program that vastly increased the food-growing capabilities of Mexico, Brazil, the Philippines, India, and many other over-populated countries, thereby averting the mass starvation of billions predicted by Malthus and by his latter-day acolyte, Professor Paul Ehrlich, whose book *The Population Bomb* had a place on many bedside tables in the Sixties and Seventies.

Norman Borlaug, who won the 1970 Nobel Peace Prize (and a slew of other high honors) for his work as the "Father of the Green Revolution," was an inveterate optimist. He believed that every problem caused by technology would have a technological solution, and that the Story of Mankind is the story of inevitable progress marked by constantly-improving prospects for universal peace and prosperity. In his public addresses, he deployed an impressive range of public health and longevity improvement statistics to prove his point. I hope he's right, but my gut tells me that the patches and smoke and mirrors that are holding the world's economy and food production system together may not be able to stave off disaster for much longer.

Borlaug's life work has come under attack by those who feel that the Green Revolution encouraged unsustainable population growth in India, China and Latin America, resulting not only in vast hordes of economic migrants to the United States and other developed countries, but also in the wrong-headed promotion of agricultural practices that ultimately destroy the land, the air and the water. Many voices today call for a rejection of genetically modified organisms, over-reliance on chemical pesticides, and livestock practices that degrade and torture our fellow mammals (and chickens even more), who are reduced to bags full of red and white meat on our supermarket shelves.

Advocates for sustainable agriculture are spitting in the wind. The die is cast; that ship has sailed; don't cry over spilt milk. Any movement away from the food production quagmires we confront will be led by McDonald's, Monsanto, Wal-Mart and Perdue Chickens, based on new research produced by the visionaries at the Rockefeller Foundation, the Gates Foundation, the Ford Foundation and the Clinton Global Initiative. As species die out as the result of over-fishing, over-farming, over-hunting, over-use of underground aquifers, oil and chemical and nuclear waste disposal in our rivers, oceans, and streams, global warming, and various unforeseeable events that represent Nature's revenge, peas will replace avocadoes in guacamole, and sushi will be made of synthetic fish flakes or raw meat rather than tuna fish, salmon or yellowtail.

It cannot be disputed that American industrial tycoons, and John D. Rockefeller's oil monopoly above all others, have created a world that faces imminent collapse. We are probably only a century or two away from the bleak landscape of *Soylent Green,* a popular science-fiction movie that depicted a world so overpopulated that surplus humans were slaughtered for food.

While the world created by God lasted for perhaps 6,000 years or so, longer than the Roman Empire, the world according to Rockefeller is running out a clock that may have only a few decades before transition to silicon-based life forms is the only option for the survival of human intelligence. The energy companies have raped and pillaged the Earth to bring us cheap gasoline, cheap electricity and cheap petrochemical products such as plastics. The impact on human health has been catastrophic, even if it has been largely hidden by statistics showing longer life spans, higher quality-of-life indicators, and more money in our pockets.

What few people realize is how much other aspects of the Rockefeller philanthropic program reinforced the damage caused to human health by the oil industry's depredations on the environment and the trashing of the planet that was an unavoidable result of wildly excessive population growth in stressed areas of the world.

Can we really trust the people who put us in this fix and made us sick to heal the planet and cure us? This is a job for Superman or Wonder Woman, who do not exist in real life. Instead, we are likely to find that persons resembling the greedy comic-strip "arch-enemies" – the Joker, the Penguin, Lex Luthor – are more often than not the characters assigned to do the mopping up jobs. The foxes are in charge of the henhouse. Because of hard-money politics, the EPA chief is often an ex-oil company lobbyist; the FDA chief is a former Bayer CEO; and it seems that nearly everyone else in the Cabinet is a banker or a banker's spouse. Our ambassadors are chosen according to how much they contributed to the President's campaign; our Senators and Congressmen come from wish lists generated by the American Enterprise Institute, Grover Norquist, Emily's List, the Tea Party and Al Sharpton; and our judges are chosen by a litmus test on abortion. Behind all of this is a small group of shadowy moneyed elders and their hired computer programmers and PR flacks and actuaries who work tirelessly to ensure that the money flows in the right direction.

The Control System is designed to be air-tight and water-tight; there are no vents or escape hatches. Breaking free is no longer possible for the nation as a whole, and the world is doomed over a shorter long haul than anyone could have imagined a few short years ago; but this does not mean that individual rebellion is hopeless or without any sense. By dint of persistence, hard work and some guidance from your neighbors and enlightened fellow citizens, you can gain greater control over your health and your wealth. The people all around you may be wrapped ever tighter in their chains; but you will gain a sense of freedom and dignity that grows greater with every step you take to wean yourself from the Nanny State and Daddy Warbucks.

Twelve

DARK MATTER

"If the right people had been in charge of Nixon's funeral, his casket would have been launched into one of those open-sewage canals that empty into the ocean just south of Los Angeles. He was a swine of a man and a jabbering dupe of a president. Nixon was so crooked that he needed servants to help him screw his pants on every morning. Even his funeral was illegal. He was queer in the deepest way. His body should have been burned in a trash bin."

— **HUNTER S. THOMPSON,** *WHERE WERE YOU WHEN THE FUN STOPPED?*

Mark Twain said it best: "there are lies, damned lies, and statistics." The Bureau of Economic Statistics is the biggest damned lie machine that has ever been built, and will doubtless remain so until Obamacare is fully implemented and we start to read about the millions of lives it saves every year.

The government can't run an honest public toilet or prison commissary. There are always skimmers and scammers and profiteers and community organizers fighting for a piece of the action from every government program. Why should Obamacare be any better?

While the lion's share of government contracts always seems to go to GE, ExxonMobil, Halliburton, IBM and other leading members of the U.S. Chamber of Commerce, it is nearly impossible to decipher the money trail of even the most useful government program. This has been greatly exacerbated by the Congressional Budget Office's adoption of "dynamic scoring," under which reporting of government expenditures and the impact of tax bills must be appropriately balanced by mathematical algorithms based on partisan wishful thinking.

The Universe is full of dark matter; the United States has a massive hidden economy. Barter transactions, the drug trade, the sex industry, and other organized crime enterprises are not featured on any balanced sheets or tax returns, but probably account for a larger percentage of economic activity than even the healthcare industries. CIA "Black Ops," Special Forces missions, NSA spying operations, secret diplomatic and trade missions, and Defense Intelligence Agency programs cost more than we will ever know, and act as a huge brake on our economic potential. We have no idea what our population is because each day brings in so many undocumented immigrants, some of them rapists from Mexico and others Asian exchange students who overstayed their visas. There are now more than 10 million such people, perhaps even double that number, who live and work in our society, but have no access to the Social Security system, no minimum wage or OSHA protections, and no right to vote. Gay marriage visas will be an additional source of immigration; if the new Trump Administration embraces bisexual polygamy/polyandry, we may yet find a way to double the population without increasing the number of citizens paying taxes and voting, and without increasing the birth rate.

Enrolling illegal immigrants and tourists in the insurance system is the next big frontier in healthcare reform, and may happen sooner rather than later. Perhaps these will be black market plans, given the challenge of covering people who have no legal mail addresses, no bank accounts, no voter ID cards, and no registered place of business. For people who have no money or bitcoin, back-breaking labor will be the price of coverage. There will be no incentive to avoid enrollment, as failure to obtain health insurance could result in being sentenced to hard labor in Arizona or at a Sunshine State prison camp, where your blood or superfluous visceral organs may be forcibly removed to provide improved care for registered healthcare insurance system participants.

When a large crowd gathers in Times Square to ring in the New Year, we also see what seems to be an equally large crowd of police officers, surveillance officers, emergency personnel and crowd control specialists. There are TV cameras on the reviewing stand platform, and hidden closed-circuit security cameras all over the neighborhood, ready to catch the first sign of public drunkenness or terrorist plots.

We should give up on the idea that the government can protect us from every danger, or provide every service we may want. To borrow a phrase from Ronald Reagan, "a government big enough to give you everything you want is a government big enough to take it all away." As bad as the big banks and the credit companies are, their repo men can't hold a candle to the IRS field agents and wage garnishers whose exorbitant penalties and fees make mincemeat of any person not part of the plutocracy who thinks tax evasion is a victimless crime.

The IRS is in a bad way these days, as its budget has been slashed in response to public indignation over aggressive collection techniques. No worries. In a classic case of healthcare mission creep, the IRS is being mobilized to enforce individual and employer mandates that guarantee the stability of our insurance system. Included among the 11,000 pages of the Affordable Care Act is a New Deal-style full employment program for tax collectors. In other words, if you don't want to opt in to healthcare reform, IRS agents and ATF agents will hunt you down and persuade you to change your mind.

None of us ever know what really happened even in the most widely known events in history. Even when the outcome of a war is clear, public opinion polls show that not everyone realizes that. Among the minority of Japanese high school history students who know that the United States and Japan fought a war, many of them answered that the winner was Japan. There are people in the South who still want to fly the Confederate battle flag. There are Frenchmen who believe that Waterloo was Napoleon's biggest victory. Some men still think their side won the battle of the sexes.

In many situations, public ignorance is fostered and aggravated by extreme government secrecy. To this day, we have no idea what really happened in Roswell, New Mexico in 1947, and what is stored in Nevada's Area 51. The recipe for atomic bombs was a secret from everyone but our leading enemies, who managed to steal it while the program was still underway. The story of the CIA's secret wars has emerged slowly over the years, and many of the details will remain blacked out forever. Whether Kennedy was killed by a single bullet or a vast conspiracy of his enemies around the world is still an open question more than a half-century after his untimely death.

Many things are not what they appear to be, even when certain damning facts are beyond dispute. While no one seriously doubts that the Monica Lewinsky episode will be remembered as a tawdry moment in Presidential history, it is equally true that no one could have suspected at the time that the men leading the charge against President Clinton – Gingrich, Livingston and Hastert – would eventually all be embroiled in equally tawdry sex scandals. In the case of Hastert, his flings with young boys came to light nearly two decades after the damage was done to Clinton.

It is widely agreed that, at least since the days of Warren Harding, no American president was more engaged in deception, corruption, secrecy, graft, bribery and other high crimes and misdemeanors than Richard Nixon. Watergate was the tip of the iceberg, one of those rare moments that allowed us to peel the skin of the onion and look inside. Nixon dodged many crises during his long political career, and each one fed his paranoia. The Nixon campaign's treasonous pre-election meetings with representatives of North Vietnam were papered over by the Nobel Committee's decision to award the Nobel Peace Prize to Henry Kissinger. Nixon was lucky that many of his political associates were so corrupt that they made him look good by comparison.

Today, after so many years of inconsequential and/or failed presidencies, Nixon has been getting another second look. This rehabilitation started long before Bill Clinton's famous words at Nixon's gravesite, where he summoned the American people to "remember President Nixon's life in totality," and urged that *the days of judging President Nixon on anything less than his entire life and career have come to a close.* Nixon is now seen as the wise statesman who ended the Vietnam War; who started the process of reconciliation with China, who promoted détente and arms control agreements with the Soviet Union.

Clinton headed the list of Nixon's achievements with his willingness to take on challenges here at home on matters from cancer research to environmental protection, putting the power of the Federal Government where Republicans and Democrats had neglected to put it in the past."

I have mixed views about Nixon's impact on the environment, which looks positive only in comparison to the ravages wrought by his successors; but Nixon's contribution in promoting the so-called War on Cancer represents one of the greatest failures of American policy during the two hundred-plus years of our history. Looking under the hood of this great crusade, we find once again that the initial funds to establish the organization that became the American Cancer Society were provided by philanthropist John D. Rockefeller in 1913, the very year that his campaign to establish the Federal Reserve System was codified into law.

The American Cancer Society was well known to elementary school children in the Sixties. First-graders were dispatched through their neighborhoods with a tin can and a pitch to "help send a mouse to college." Spare coins that had been going to missionaries ministering to the starving children of Africa were redirected to the medical research labs of Rockefeller University and Sloan-Kettering. Rockefeller wanted his dimes back!

Despite all this talk of war, progress against cancer, like progress against ISIS, has been halting, incremental, elusive, and limited. While the long-term survival rates for some forms of cancer have increased, many of the treatments invented during the hundred-year War on Cancer have only managed to prolong suffering, and some of them only hasten death by adding to the poisons tearing down the body. Faith healers and prayer healers and psychic healers and stem cell quacks in Mexico have done even worse than the failed medical establishment.

Some cancers are probably unavoidable because of environmental or genetic factors that weaken the immune system of people. Cancers associated with old age will inevitably increase as the U.S. population ages, and nothing much can be done to prevent cancer among people who insist on smoking or who live in houses built with toxic materials. That does not mean that we should resign ourselves to giving up our personal fight against this deadly and poorly understood disease.

More and more, we are learning that diet is the culprit in many of the worst cancers. Pancreatic cancer is associated with a love of red meat, butter and milk. Even AIDS, which devastates the immune system and renders its victims more susceptible to cancer, can be incredibly exacerbated or mitigated by a person's dietary choices.

We should not rely on the expensive, corrupt and largely clueless healthcare establishment to bail us out once we have a cancer diagnosis. Every day you put off steps to prevent disease is a day you are taking away from your life. The scientists at Rockefeller University will announce major breakthroughs every day from now till doomsday, but each day between now and doomsday will see a greater toll of cancer victims.

Instead of waiting patiently for a miracle drug that will likely never come, we should focus more effort on how to avoid eating foods that cause our cells to mutate, and how to add to our diet foods that inhibit and reverse the growth of cancer. Winning the War on Cancer will not be achieved by simply pouring money down the rat hole of government-sponsored rodent research. I think our best chance for victory lies with making healthy lifestyle choices every day, and the primary goal of this book is to help steer you in that direction.

Thirteen

"They have people at the bank, they go, "OK, some of these people don't have enough money, so we better take their money from them because they have so little." That's it. There's no explanation better than that. If you have a lot of money, they give you money just for having it. They go, "Here, take this guy's $15 – the hell with him. What the hell's he doing with it? He's just wasting our time."

— **Louis C.K.,** *"Not Enough Money to Have Money."*

"Naked came I out of my mother's womb, and naked shall I return thither: the Lord gave, and the Lord hath taken away; blessed be the name of the Lord."

— Job *1:21*

The big banks – Chase, Citibank, Bank of America – are always raising minimum account balances and fees for failing to maintain these balances. They grant or deny credit cards, mortgages and home-refinancing loans based on your credit score and presentation of acceptable collateral.

Minimum monthly payments for your credit cards start out comfortably low, and are suddenly jacked up after a year; or even after a month if you fail to make one on time. Interest rates on consumer credit cards may be double or even triple what it costs the bank to borrow money. A check drawn on another bank may take a week or more to clear, depending on where you live.

When you walk into a Chase branch and get online to deposit a check, you often find that the stack of deposit slips has disappeared, meaning that you have to ask a branch associate to get you one. This is a "manufactured shortage," a simple ploy to get you to approach a personal banker, who will sit you down and try to cross-sell you Chase's proprietary investment products. What should be a two-minute trip to cash a check turns into a very expensive half hour, which is followed up with scores of e-mails and telephone calls to make sure you are happy and get you to buy more junk bonds or CDs. As the banker gets to know you, she will ask you for referrals to your friends and colleagues so she can hit them with the same relentless sales pitch.

Healthcare is getting to be much the same; and these trends are accelerating as banks invest in insurance companies, hospitals and pharmaceutical companies. When you go to the doctor with a sore throat, you end up with a referral to a pathology lab, an appointment for an eye exam and a recommendation for an experimental lupus vaccine. In the future, when your health insurance information, medical history and financial records are all stored in your scannable implanted chip, doctors may feel free to treat your body as an ATM, offering medical treatment commensurate with the amount of money currently in your bank account.

For those with a lot of money, this may turn out to be a great thing. Doctors will give discounts on certain usually costly procedures because they don't want to kill the cash cow. You may be able to afford custom medicines and artificial replacement organs synthesized specifically for you by careful scientific examination of your genetic map. If you are lucky, you may even live to be as old as David Rockefeller, who celebrated his 101st birthday on June 12, 2016.

For those who have no money, or whose insurance is Obamacare Basic, doctors will recite a litany of procedures that would be nice if you could afford them. Then they will shout, "Next!"

We already have phony expiration dates on over-the-counter pill bottles. In the years to come, we will have medical devices with expiration dates. If your payments are not made on time, your pacemaker and your heart will stop functioning.

The future has a lot of great things in store for us. There will be space travel for millionaires; new forms of interactive pornography; and even cooler apps on our cellphones. Woody Allen's "orgasmatron" is a possibility; a likelier possibility is the marketing of silicon-based robot dolls created by 3D printing processes to match every nook and cranny of Annie Sprinkle's or John Leslie's body. A schlub like Arnold Horshack could bed a digitally-enhanced version of Joe Dimaggio's ex-wife. Lovemaking would become as safe as safe sex with yourself; and as exciting as fireworks on the 4th of July. These new systems will surely be sold on a subscription model; failure to feed the meter will result in a high level of frustration.

One way to deal with sexual frustration is to pour cold water on yourself; rebranded as the "ice bucket challenge," this same simple procedure raised millions of dollars for ALS research. These days, marketing gimmicks for healthcare dot every street corner; and Cialis or Vagisil ads pop up constantly on your computer screen or television set.

The Golden Era of television featured a Jerry Lewis telethon once a year; other than that, the only time you heard about doctors and medical procedures was during episodes of *M*A*S*H*, *General Hospital or Marcus Welby, MD*. All that changed with the declaration of the War on Cancer.

When Richard Nixon, the all-time champion of corrupt politics, signed the National Cancer Act of 1971, it was the beginning of the end for honest medicine.

The creation of what we know now as the Food and Drug Administration in 1906 is usually presented as the uplifting story of Progressive politics triumphing over the horrors of the deadly practices of the sloppy meat-packing industry revealed by Upton Sinclair in *The Jungle*. The FDA now regulates about 25% of the consumer goods sold in the United States. The back story is more complicated. While Dupont famously celebrates the miracles of "better life through chemistry," no one has been better able to take advantage of chemistry than the Rockefellers.

The wedge to take over the drug industry was the co-option of the American Medical Association. By replacing the crucifix with the caduceus, with doctors the priests of the new religion of scientific rationalism, the Rockefeller medical education system, which had founded and funded many of the leading hospitals nationwide, insisted on the need to control not only the number of doctors, but also the right to access and distribute prescription drugs. The FDA became an adjunct of the patent system. The process for getting a drug approved became increasingly arduous, while the penalties for using non-approved medicines, devices and treatment methods became increasingly subject not only to ridicule, but to severe legal and financial sanctions enforced by the government. Since natural substances could not be patented or approved by the FDA, pursuing such non-toxic treatments was not financially rewarding. By creating a medical education system where drug research needs determine how patients are treated, the Rockefellers created a huge market for drugs, to the point where many Americans literally depend on pills to survive from one day to the next.

Once a patient begins with the allopathic drug regimen, the process of drug addiction resembles alcoholism or narcotic drug dependency. Gateway drugs lead to ever more potent concoctions as patients develop a tolerance or fail to respond to a particular prescription. Drugs that cause mood swings will be supplemented with drugs to rebalance emotions. Drugs that may cause harm to the liver may require further procedures or treatments to counteract those effects.

Cancer, the "emperor of all maladies," is perhaps best described as the king of iatrogenic diseases. Carcinogens include not only well-known poisonous substances such as nicotine, but also various chemicals that have been introduced to our environment in an effort to protect us from other health problems. Fluoridating the water has caused a 40% reduction in childhood cavities, but there are studies that indicate the possibility of an elevated risk of osteosarcoma in male rats exposed to elevated levels of sodium fluoride; and there has long been a fierce debate over whether and to what extent sodium fluoride and other chemicals in the water supply present a public health risk that may override the benefits alleged to exist. Chlorine is another chemical that is commonly used to rid water of pathogens, and it has also been linked to higher levels of rectal and bladder cancer. Perhaps the only safe way to enjoy your swimming pool is to add butt plugs and water-tight genital wraps to the goggles and ear plugs swimmers commonly use.

Industrialization creates new sources of cancer-causing substances with every new wave of energy development or mining rush. Fracking, which industry lobbyists say is completely safe, produces not only earthquakes in places that have had none for centuries, but also neighborhoods where the drinking water has a powerful chemical smell and can be readily burned. Mining towns often have to deal with greatly elevated levels of arsenic in their water.

Other carcinogens include x-rays, a mainstay of dental offices and emergency rooms. Industrial pollution, including the emissions from pharmaceutical plants, contributes further to the cancer epidemic. Medications that weaken or compromise the immune system are an ever-present danger. Some of the most serious carcinogens are the radiation and chemotherapy treatments commonly used to treat cancer!

The dirty little secret of cancer research in the Seventies, and even today, is that cancer is an intractable problem. Once you get a diagnosis of late-stage cancer, you are better off calling a priest than a doctor. Cancer doctors throw all kinds of poison – radiation, toxic chemicals, God knows what else – in the vain hope of extending a person's life by a month or two. Usually, the side effects kill the patient at about the same time as the cancer would have claimed her. Basically, a sick person gets to endure two diseases instead of one.

Since cancer is one of the nation's top two killer diseases – with the other being coronary disease – doctors have had ample opportunity to experiment on people as well as on mice. The pressure to show results comes not only from desperate patients, but also from hospital administrators and institute leaders who want new NIH money for black hole research. Researchers grab at straws; if one patient lives a few weeks longer than another one, statistical analysis techniques are deployed to make it seem that the team has identified a highly promising area for further endless research. Patients are then bombarded with higher and higher doses of poisons that can't possibly benefit them, and huge piles of money are banked by all involved in the Cancer War game.

A patient who is cured is useless to the medical establishment. Hospitals only make money from sick people, so they have little or no incentive to make people healthy, at least not too quickly. The allopathic Control System favors chronic diseases, diseases that require constant doses of medicine and repeated hospital stays. Cancer represents the jackpot in that regard.

Specialist doctors at research hospitals don't know their patients. Many oncologists develop an affable and compassionate bedside manner, but the nature of their work means that they often become inured to death and don't go out of their way to prevent it. They are trained to be observers more than actors in a human drama.

Why do patients tolerate such indignities? The answer has to do with the creation of a set of rituals and symbols that lead a patient to accept a doctor's authority, even when her body tells her that what is being done to her is making her condition worse, not better. People are trained to worship at the altar of the white coat. A stethoscope, which in most instances is about as useful as a pinky ring, signals to the patient that she is in the hands of someone who knows the secrets of life and death. Specialists in oncology or AIDS or pediatric neurology have degrees from the nation's best universities displayed prominently on their walls. Winning a Nobel Prize in Medicine is almost a required credential for a teaching position at Rockefeller University, just as much as a PhD is a basic credential for an adjunct position at Harvard College.

In my experience, fancy degrees and stethoscopes make little difference to a patient's prospects for recovery. Getting admitted to a hospital for cancer is often just the first procedure in carrying out a death sentence. Hospitals, like prisons, thrive on volume. They need to make a good amount per patient in order to maintain financial health, which is the only kind of health that really matters to them.

Health comes from within. If you don't have a healthy lifestyle, a positive outlook, and a proactive attitude about listening to your body and learning about your disease, putting yourself in the hands of the so-called experts is more often than not simply a path to your financial and personal obliteration.

As terrible as many allopathic doctors are, they are a damned sight better than the lawyers and actuaries who are their co-equal partners in your care at the local clinic or medical center. Although I hate much of what passes as "modern medicine," because I believe too many doctors are pummeling their patients' bodies with substances that harm them as often as they cure them, I feel that there is a special place in hell for people whose main job in patient care is to figure out the most efficient way to avoid paying medical claims; how to make a doctor an assembly line robot; and how to avoid responsibility when a patient is harmed by improper treatments. That is my objection to the trends in medical practice that are now being consolidated under the name of Obamacare. My "spider sense" tells me that healthcare reform has been designed under the leadership of the AMA and the Rockefeller Foundation as basically a means of getting the government to act as a blank-check ATM for wealthy interests.

Now that we have Donald Trump as President, I don't know what he has in mind for healthcare, but I sure hope he does not promote the kind of healthcare reform that only serves to deepen our misery and serves only the Control System. In many ways I am happy about his success. As the first non-politician President, his example will be a powerful role model for other business men. I think he will do his best to keep the nation out of war, even though I have some concerns that he is a little too trigger-happy for my taste. On energy policy, I think he will continue to promote higher mileage standards for vehicles and airplanes. Even though it is probably already far too late for government policies to have any meaningful impact as far as avoiding the worst consequences of global warming, I am cheered that he takes seriously the words of Pope Francis: "The Earth, our home, is beginning to look like an immense pile of filth."

The Pope's statement could be made with equal justice about our bodies and minds (and, he would probably add, our souls). As a child, I experienced the vivid impact of the famous TV commercial depicting an Indian brave canoeing through a river filled with garbage. The tag line of this commercial was: "People start pollution; people can stop it." My impression of the dignity of the Native American respect for Mother Earth is part of what gave me the impetus to study the old ways of medicine men in Western and Eastern cultures. I feel like that teared-up Indian when I think about the billions of tons of toxic chemicals that make their way into our bloodstreams, both through the intentional administration of medicines, vaccines, water treatments with fluoride or chlorine; and inadvertently, as these and other household and industrial chemicals leak into our food supply, into our water, and into the very air we breathe. My gut told me that there was a better way, and my experience over the years has borne that out.

Louis XIV famously said, "L'état, c'est moi." John D. Rockefeller's version of that sentiment was similarly concise: "God gave me my money." As we all know, God helps those who help themselves, and John D. Rockefeller was certainly no exception to that rule. In 1880, at the height of his business career, Rockefeller said, "The age of combination is here to stay. Individualism has gone, never to return."

Rockefeller's vision, or lack thereof, created a world where the overwhelming majority of us are the human equivalent of lab rats, subject to the whims of the Control System, which decides who will live and who will die, and in what fashion and when. Throwing off this tyranny will require more than public will, because money always triumphs over people in a system rigged to the degree ours is. John D. Rockefeller became a rich man through managing competition and controlling the market for kerosene refining. He got even richer as the Model T expanded the need for oil. What put him over the top and made him the world's first billionaire were the U.S. government's efforts at "trust-busting," which broke up Standard Oil, but left Rockefeller as the largest shareholder in most of the daughter companies. That experience was one of many that taught the Rockefeller family and their fellow magnates that the key to expanding their piece of the pie was to make sure that the laws and regulations are written in such a way as to contradict the public purposes that led to their enactment.

Hillary Clinton and Barack Obama are the products of a century of Rockefeller investment in higher education, which focused on elevating the role of women and minorities. The University of Chicago, where Obama taught, was founded by John D. Rockefeller, who is probably looking down on the White House with a great big smile. Hillary Clinton has now spent several years mastering the foundation business that solidified the Rockefeller legacy in the United States.

Since Obamacare went into effect, four of the nation's largest insurance companies have become two of the nation's largest insurance companies, and chances are that these too shall merge. Rate increase requests that were surprisingly modest during the early stages of ACA implementation now resemble the inexorable Ivy League tuition rate increases of the 1990s or the steep oil price increases of 1973.

Bill Cosby's *modus operandi* was to allegedly drug women prior to having his way with them. The Rockefeller-built allopathic medical treatment system is designed to work in the same way, but on a much larger scale than the sexual predator behind Dr. Huxtable's affable mask. The certificates and diplomas on the wall, the reassuring bedside manner and the shiny new equipment are designed to tranquilize the patient. Prescription drugs, which may seem innocent enough at first, over time paralyze the patient's will and numb the body. The final episode may not be a lethal injection *per se,* although that certainly happens from time to time. More often, patients are kept in a semi-zombie state, often for many years, where they are dependent on drugs and radiation treatments long past the point when they would have survived under natural conditions. Whether they are in a medically-induced coma or in a constant state of severe pain or deep in the grip of dementia, America's seniors (and juniors who get hooked on the system early) are like lab rats, kept artificially alive to boost the "success" statistics measured by longevity on the calendar rather than vitality within. Their diseases are used as gimmicks to attract research dollars to the medical research institutes, which are often the beneficiaries not only of the money flowing from "advanced" patient treatment in the hospitals, but also of legacies bequeathed and raised by families grateful for Grandma's extra years of life: "In lieu of flowers, please send a check to the American Cancer Society."

More and more, people will come to the realization that alternative medicine, like alternative energy, is one of the central pillars of a better future. The human species may not have much longer to rule the Earth, but I believe we should live out these remaining years in the most dignified and satisfying way possible, by focusing on a vision of what constitutes true psychic and physical health.

My goal as a Doctor of Chiropractic is to empower people to take control of their own health by filling their minds with noble thoughts and nurturing their bodies with proper attention to nutrition, posture and exercise. The body is very resilient, but occasionally things go wrong. When something is out of kilter, you should educate yourself about possible underlying causes and natural remedies. When you come to an impasse every now and then, I am here to help guide you in your search for true healing.

You cannot stave off a lab rat future by developing a prescription drug habit early in life. You need to start early by developing healthy habits: "an apple a day keeps the doctor away." An over-fertilized fig tree will not bear fruit; in the same way, an over-medicated patient is a person who will always be sick. Alternative medicine provides cures, not treatments. The body is designed to resist attacks from the environment. The key to leading a long and healthy life is to nurture your immune system. This means suffering some minor aches and pains with patience. Natural remedies may not always be immediately efficacious as some of the drug options now available, but we do not need an atomic bomb to knock down a tree. Putting potent chemical substances into your system generates a cascade effect that will incapacitate you more and more.

It is too easy to become a slave to the body's weaknesses rather than a free person making healthy decisions. One of the worst things you can do to yourself is to become dependent on drugs. Whether these drugs are recreational or therapeutic, they throw off your body's natural immune defenses and make you that much more susceptible to the next shock that comes your way. Don't let this happen to you!

The cure for obesity is not a fat pill or a stomach stapling operation. Diet and exercise are much more effective. The best allergy treatments are not inhalers full of chemicals or pills that make you drowsy. There are plenty of natural substances that relieve allergy symptoms without exposing you to side effects.

We are asking the healthcare system to deliver more than it can or should. A broken leg will not heal on its own; but a cold or flu usually will disappear after a few days of rest. You should learn to listen to your body by getting familiar with how it works. If you feel something unusual, and it is not severe chest pains or labor contractions, go to a medical reference library or the Internet to learn for yourself what might be causing such symptoms. Talk about medical issues among friends. They may have great suggestions based on their own experience. As you learn, pass that knowledge on to family, friends and colleagues.

If you feel you need a doctor's advice or a prescription for poison ivy or a spider bite, why not try telemedicine? Ninety to ninety-five percent of issues for which people visit a doctor's office could be resolved at a fraction of the cost by a simple telephone call to a licensed physician. The AMA is fighting this industry relentlessly, and state medical boards have tried to limit telemedicine' s scope and availability, because the Control System needs you in the doctor's office or hospital so that its over-stressed doctors can figure out how to tap further into your insurance money.

Don't be afraid of medical issues. They are part of the human condition. We all have an obligation to learn about health, to take proper care of ourselves and to encourage others to do the same. Don't wait until you have a baseball-sized tumor on your forehead to go to a hospital. The moment you suspect something is wrong, look it up. If the cause seems unclear, by all means consult with a doctor to find out whether you have a disease and what it is. That doesn't mean you should just blindly swallow whatever pills she prescribes for you. Once you know what the disease is called, go to the library or do a Google search. See what other people say about their experiences with it. When possible, find out whether there is a natural remedy for ridding your body of these symptoms. When you find something that works for you, spread the word.

Computers are a wonderful tool for work and for play, but spending all day long staring at a video terminal or phone screen is not healthy. By the same token, there are great things about modern medicine. Make the doctor your friend, not your guru or your controller. He does not have all the answers. Remember that he is there to make money, not to cure people. If he sees that you take an active interest in your own health, he may be able to contribute to your self-knowledge, but you can't expect your doctor to care about you if you don't care about yourself.

You should make healthcare decisions based on reason, not emotion. Drugs cloud your judgment, and lead you to do things you know are bad for you. By giving insurance companies, banks, doctors and drug companies *carte blanche* to make of your health what they will, by launching you on a path that leads to greater and greater dependence on expensive prescription medicines, you set yourself up for terrible disappointments.

Well-being is not just a matter of absence of pain or having a long life measured by number of years listed on your tombstone or crematory inscription. A healthy lifestyle requires balanced nutrition, active participation in exercise and sports, positive relationships with family and friends, and a lively intellectual life, which will often be bolstered by time set aside for meditation, reflection and prayer.

I am not advising anybody to rely on the power of prayer and positive thinking to treat a broken leg or a gunshot wound. Modern medicine has its limitations; but it cannot be denied that there are many situations or conditions that require or benefit from the intervention of a trained surgeon or obstetrician.

I am not recommending to anyone to either vaccinate or not vaccinate their children against common childhood diseases; but I strongly suggest that you study reports about the efficacy and potential side effects of any vaccination that for one reason or another has become controversial. Once you have had a chance to consider such issues and weigh the risks against the benefits, you will be better able to reach the right decisions for you and your family.

The important thing is that you should realize that your health is your responsibility. Donald Trump won't take care of you when you feel sick. The American medical system has been set up as a money-generating system by wealthy people who want all your money. The government, the insurance companies, and the banks already have too much power over the American people: they can lock you up and throw away the key; they are coming for your guns; they are ready to seize your house when you miss your mortgage payments or taxes. Now they want to expand their grip on the healthcare system by wiping out all competition from those of us who believe that the system that exists is failing us. Don't let yourself become one of their lab rats! The fight to take back our healthcare system is a fight for our freedom. It is an uphill battle, but we are a people of strong backbone. Charge!

Fourteen

GENERATION SICK

"Patients were not people. They were profit centers."

— FEDERAL PROSECUTORS, REFERRING TO DR.
FARID FATA, AN ONCOLOGIST WHO PERFORMED
UNNECESSARY TREATMENTS ON HIS PATIENTS

*"Something startling is happening to middle-aged white Americans.
Unlike every other age group, unlike every other racial and
ethnic group, unlike their counterparts in other rich countries,
death rates in this group have been rising, not falling...[R]ising
annual death rates among this group are being driven not by the
big killers like heart disease and diabetes but by an epidemic of
suicides and afflictions stemming from substance abuse: alcoholic
liver disease and overdoses of heroin and prescription opioids."*

— GINA KOLATA, FRONT PAGE ARTICLE IN THE
NOVEMBER 2, 2015 EDITION OF THE NEW YORK TIMES

B efore Ivan Pavlov, most animal experiments at the Imperial Institute
of Experimental Medical in Saint Petersburg involved the study of

"acute" conditions. Scientist would inject some chemical substance into a cat or dog, and then open up the animal to see the effects. Lab rats didn't last long in those days. Pavlov wanted to study normal physiological processes such as the digestive process and gastric function of dogs under different conditions. This required employing the same animal at different times, which meant that Pavlov's laboratory needed to keep his experimental subjects alive in order to conduct his "chronic" experiments.

Pavlov's big contribution to science was based on his observation that animals tended to salivate before eating their food. He discovered that he could stimulate salivation merely by ringing a dinner bell, once the dogs had been "conditioned" to link the sound of the bell to an expectation of feeding.

Pavlov's Nobel Prize-winning work opened the door to widespread experimentation on people. During the twentieth century, psychology and chemistry became more important than anatomy and physiology in the practice of medicine. Mind-altering drugs were among the century's greatest breakthroughs. Hallucinogens such as LSD; narcotic opioid painkillers such as Oxycodone, heroin, and marijuana; and tranquilizers such as Quaaludes, Xanax and Valium; all these became household names, not only for the pain and anxiety they relieved, but for the sexual hijinks and crime waves that accompanied their spread among the population. Prescription painkiller overdoses are one of the leading causes of death among young people. Each year, these wonder drugs kill about as many people – roughly 30,000 - as traffic accidents or gun violence (homicides and suicides combined).

Drug companies have many ways to get inside your body by getting inside your head. "Plop, plop, fizz, fizz, oh what a relief it is." Any viewer of network TV is subjected to a daily barrage of feel-good ads for products that are basically a combination of chemicals that target the pain and pleasure centers of your brain in order to alleviate or cause selected symptoms as desired. Most old men will not get a four-hour erection from a little blue pill; blurred vision or blindness is more likely. Nevertheless, that warning is in every sexual stimulant commercial because it sounds like winning the lottery to a guy who typically spends half an hour trying to achieve a one-minute erection that instantly disappears when confronted by the nagging image of his actual spouse.

Sugary sodas have long been recognized as one of the leading causes of the obesity epidemic. Researchers put lab rats through the paces and found a chemical solution that was marketed as "diet soda." It turns out that diet sodas trigger fat production enzymes at an even higher rate than regular Pepsi or Coke!

For many years, aspirin, a bitter pill made from a chemical found in willow bark, was the pain reliever of choice. Now that much stronger and more effective pain relievers are sold over-the-counter, aspirin is mainly used as a fever reducer for babies and children and as a prophylactic against cardiac disease and strokes among people over 50, particularly among those who have experienced heart attacks or are considered high risk.

Aspirin seemed to work OK for headaches, but among its unpleasant side effects were episodes of gastrointestinal bleeding in some patients. It also didn't do much for people who were experiencing cramps and muscle aches. Fortunately, ibuprofen and naproxen sodium came along. These new wonderful drugs zapped the aches and pains of daily life. Under brand names such as Advil, Motrin and Aleve, they made fortunes for several pharmaceutical companies, and they hold an honored place in the medicine cabinets of people all over the world. Unfortunately, the FDA finally realized that these potent non-aspirin pain relievers are associated with elevated risk of heart disease and strokes, meaning that the more of them you take, the more likely you are to need aspirin to block their side effects!

Drug addiction is not just for junkies anymore. From the gateway drugs like children's Tylenol to the AZT cocktails that treat AIDS is for many in our society a tragically short path. It often seems as if the discovery of new medical conditions and super-bugs increases faster than the development of new vaccines and drugs to treat them. While life expectancy at birth slowly increases from year to year, the chances for each newborn to develop a chronic long-term illness at some point in her life seem to go up exponentially. While our ancestors may have had an occasional swig of brandy to ward off colds, most of us today have boxes full of sleeping pills, topical anti-itch creams, cough syrup, lice kits, antibiotics, and an assortment of other formulations that vary with age, gender and personality type. When we actually get sick, the medicine bottles pile up in the refrigerator, on the kitchen table, and on the windowsills. For those unfortunate enough to have a chronic disease, the very furniture takes on the appearance of a robot war. There are giant oxygen tanks, adjustable beds, wheelchairs, walkers, prostheses, and various testing kits. The dressers are full of adult diapers, colostomy bags, air fresheners and other paraphernalia designed to assist in the management of the relentlessly creeping stench of death. Instead of books and office supplies, shelves and desks are covered with hospital bills and post-it notes to remember doctor's appointments, dose times and even the names of loved ones as the mind slowly disappears.

Given that the alternative to life support is death, most of us accept these burdens with equanimity. Some of us, however, see this train wreck coming and try to change course before it is too late.

Personal responsibility for your health is the key to a long and happy life. While there is always the chance any given day that you will get the armed chamber in the Russian roulette game that is the human condition, there is plenty you can do to minimize the chances that you end up as a lump of flesh slobbering out bodily fluids and saliva as you are wheeled and pushed from one doctor to another. Leo Ornstein was writing new piano sonatas at the age of 102. The average centenarian, of whom there are tens of thousands in the United States, has a cerebellum that is epigenetically 15 years younger than would be expected. Most of these people grew up in a time when drugs were not commonly used to treat illness, or at least not every imaginable illness. They survived epidemics that carried off many of their peers, thereby perhaps strengthening their immune systems.

A long life without health and well-being is basically a slow death sentence. To avoid pain later, you should learn to tolerate some pain today. "No pain, no gain" is a slogan we should live by in realms beyond weight-lifting. Daily exercise and proper nutrition are a must. There are no quick and easy shortcuts. Like Dorian Gray's portrait, your body will sooner or later show the evidence if you abuse it with chemicals. Steroids that pump up your muscles can also make you impotent. Fad diets that rely on "vitamin shakes" are generally doomed to failure because chocolate-flavored drinks train your body to crave exactly the wrong things.

The pharmaceutical companies have set up a vast labyrinth of testing labs all over the world. It often seems that most of them are in New Jersey, where the laws against toxic waste dumps and chemical pollution and oil spills are apparently quite a bit less stringent than in New York or California. As tort reform and environmental deregulation and hunger for drug money takes hold in Alabama and North Carolina and Texas, more and more people outside New Jersey can aspire to careers as professional human guinea pigs.

Once a drug has been shown not to explode on contact with cultured human tissue, and has been proven to cause some desirable effect in mice without killing them, randomized clinical studies are performed in hospitals in Italy or Budapest. Assuming a 100% survival rate over the course of a six-week study, the stage is set for a clinical study in Princeton or Rahway. Healthy young men over 18 and under 30 volunteer to take a pill or two a day and perhaps to have themselves attached to an IV for a week or two in exchange for a check in the amount of anywhere from $500 to $1,500, more if the study requires hospitalization. They give copious blood samples, marrow samples, stool samples, urine samples and whatever other samples doctors want. Nurses hook them up to blood pressure cuffs, EEG machines, and stationary bikes; in special cases, volunteers may undergo X-rays, CAT scans, MRIs, ultrasounds and various additional high-tech procedures.

As much as possible, the labs try to screen out drugs addicts or people who are chronically ill. Generally, one type of medication or treatment is administered to a healthy young man in the prime of life. If he starts vomiting uncontrollably or coughing up blood, the study may be suspended, but in most cases the volunteer experiences nothing more than a few bouts of diarrhea, meaning that the drug is ready for public consumption.

There are few things short of a bullet to the brain that will cause the metabolism of a healthy young man to slow down much. For that reason, a lot of questionable stuff gets green-lighted fairly quickly. Once these "safe and effective" drugs are on the market, however, they are primarily used by sick people and weak people, people who in some cases could be killed by a bee sting or an overdose of peanut butter. Even people who don't look too bad are often taking three or four other drugs that may have unexpected "interactions" with the new miracle pill. That means that the real experiments take place once a drug company has tested, re-tested, bribed, lobbied and pressured to get its formulations in the eager hands of patients.

If ordinary people start to go haywire, there may arise a groundswell of support to add a warning label or some fine print cautions on the side of the box. In extreme circumstances, companies may be ordered to re-call or reformulate a drug in response to complaints. For the most part, though, a drug, once it is approved, will be marketed relentlessly by TV pitchmen and travelling salesmen until loss of patent protection renders it unprofitable and therefore unsafe and ineffective.

Drug testing is big business, and pharmaceutical companies employ phalanxes of lawyers to ram their suppositories and applicators up your ass and into your mouth and nose. They use all the tools of a modern political campaign or major jury trial. There are market research teams, psycholo-gists, and professional grant writers gainfully employed to game the system and ensure a favorable result. Former FDA administrators offer their con-nections and their knowledge of the process in exchange for a modest fee that is many times what they made when they worked for the government.

The cornucopia of drugs we find on the shelves at the local Walgreens or CVS brings quick symptom relief for allergies and minor aches and pains, whether by deceiving the senses, easing the mind, or helping an im-patient person remain calm while waiting for the immune system to do its work. The myriad substances behind the prescription counter are intended to control and treat more serious problems. There are blood thinners and thickeners; blood pressure relievers and elevators; anti-depressants; anti-seizure medications; libido enhancers (plenty of those!); and a wide variety of extra-strength pain relievers. For the really strong stuff, including radia-tion therapies, chemotherapy and implanted medical devices, you need to go to a hospital.

Intuitively, we know that ingesting all these substances, some with strange and some with catchy names, may trigger symptoms that require treatment with other prophylactics and chemical substances. In the worst cases, we have heard, a simple diet pill may cause cancer. Why, then, are so many people not only willing to take these chances, but also willing to endure the additional treatments that may be required without batting an eyelash when things start to go drastically wrong?

The answer is simple, and was provided largely by Pavlov. In a word: conditioning. Just as a dog can be trained to salivate on cue, humans have been trained to have tremendous respect for authority. A policeman or a lawyer can do with impunity things that would put another man in jail. A government official is held to far lower moral standards than the rest of us because of the trappings and privileges of her position. The medical profession, more than any other, has taken on the symbols of rank and authority in a way that allows doctors to get their clients-patients to surrender to them decisions of life and death. From the diploma on the wall to the "M.D." nameplate on the door, every detail of the doctor/patient interaction has been designed in such a way as to build and maintain confidence in the wisdom and superior will of the medical practitioner.

Today's doctors need to be as versed in psychology as in the physical treatment aspects of medicine. When a patient walks through the door of a medical clinic, the doctor's job is not only to find an effective way to deal with whatever symptoms she may present, but also how to convince her to accept a treatment plan that will ensure a profitable medical practice. This means many follow-up visits even for the most minor foot problem or allergic reaction.

While doctors have not yet evolved to the point where they can read your mind, they certainly have access to a range of information about your body that you cannot easily understand. Their blood panels and autonomic nervous system scans nearly always yield at least one value that requires subsequent monitoring or further action. Once you take the bait, they are only too pleased to find other ways to optimize your health by means of drugs that can substitute for recommended but very difficult behavioral changes.

It is only the rare rogue doctor who knowingly prescribes unneeded chemotherapy or unnecessary amputations. Another type of rogue doctor prescribes Oxycodone to his corner drug dealer. A third type of rogue doctor may overbill Medicare or Medicaid for procedures that may or may not have been necessary. There are many more doctors who do things by the book, but are nonetheless unwitting rogues, either because the patient had an unexpected reaction, or because fatigue or carelessness caused a slip of the pen, tongue or hand. While doctors certainly save many lives, at least for a time, it cannot be denied that among the leading causes of premature death today are medical error and hospital-borne infections.

Insurance companies have stringent standards of cost-effectiveness and somewhat laxer standards of quality of care that often mean that top specialists are excluded from all but the so-called platinum plans. Put another way, doctors who are well-known or well-located and therefore can command high fees often opt out of insurance because the rates are too low.

The bottom line is that you enter the medical system at your peril. If you are the kind of person who does not take regular exercise and eat a balanced diet, and if on top of that you are not knowledgeable enough to sift through the information you should possess as a consumer of medical services, you may quickly find yourself addicted to appointments, to drugs and to operations. If you want the best, you may quickly find yourself in bankruptcy court. If you want to settle for something other than the best, you may fall in the hands of one of the rogue types listed above.

A medical consumer should also be a student of psychology. You have to know the rules of the game in order to have a chance of winning, and you have to be keenly aware, with respect to the entire system, that it is rigged against you. The house always wins. Since the prize is your continued health and well-being, there is no excuse for ignorance of how the system works.

First and foremost, you should recognize that you are not simply a an artillery testing ground, ready to receive one bomb after the other. If the silver bullet hits you in the wrong spot, your life is over. While people are quite resilient when it comes to resisting natural pathogens and the aches and pains of daily life, the curveballs thrown at us in the form of acid rain, bad pill batches, improper dosing and unintentional overdoses, arsenic and PCBs in the water supply, GMOs and chemical pesticides in our fruits and vegetables, second-hand and first-hand smoke, Fukushima and Chernobyl fallout, cursory or non-existent meat and poultry inspections, ozone holes, and all the other headline and footnote dangers of modern life make it impossible to know with any certainty whether you will live to fight another day, even if you avoid the shark-infested waters of Eastern Long Island or stay inside during lightning storms. Sitting next to an Ebola patient on a plane from Chicago to Detroit might mean that you have two more weeks, unless the co-pilot gets a suicide urge or terrorists find a way to storm the cockpit.

Drinking Jim Jones' cyanide-laced Kool-Aid or swallowing a Quaalude from Bill Cosby turned out to be highly inadvisable. Chemicals designed to kill are pretty effective, as demonstrated by the mustard gas that blinded Hitler and killed some of his comrades, and the chemical weapons that Saddam Hussein used against Iran. Even chemicals intended only to produce rubber or glue, such as the methyl isocyanate implicated in the Bhopal disaster; or to clear the jungle of grass, such as the "Agent Orange" defoliant used in Vietnam, created monumental health problems and loss of life.

We all know that atomic bombs kill in an instant, as happened in Hiroshima and Nagasaki, and as would perhaps happen in Israel if Iran, Saudi Arabia, or any other of the dozens of Islamic countries or terrorist groups develops and uses a nuclear bomb in the reckless manner described by Tom Cotton and other leading lights in the Republican Party. These headlines suck up most of the oxygen, but so-called low-level exposures to these staples of modern life – chemical poisons and radiation – may end up wiping more people off the face of the Earth more quickly than has ever been deemed possible in human history.

People who live near nuclear weapons factories and waste sites grow used to seeing milk cows with tumors bigger than their udders. Their daughters lose their appetites and throw up dinner every night. Even the low-level radiation from nuclear power plants has been implicated, most famously by the nuclear physicist Dr. Ernest Sternglass, in higher incidence of childhood cancer. Dr. Sternglass's sensational 1969 article in Esquire magazine claimed that 400,000 infants had been killed by nuclear fallout from atmospheric testing and power plants; and his statement that fallout from the deployment and use of an ABM system would kill all the children in the United States proved a major spur to arms control.

Today's counterpart to the nuclear fallout problem is the global warming debate. Ninety-nine percent of scientists say that global warming is anthropogenic; the other one percent is like the groups of rogue doctors mentioned above. A few years ago, many people believed that it was useless to regulate or try to limit carbon dioxide emissions, because methane was a more potent warming gas, and methane pollution could only be reduced by changing the American diet, since the largest single contributor of atmospheric methane was cow farts. Today, we are aware of an even bigger stash of methane buried under the Arctic glaciers. If these glaciers melt as anticipated, in a methane and carbon dioxide-fueled process expected to take between two and 50 years, some climate experts say that the enormous rise in sea level will eventually overwhelm nearly all the world's coastal cities – New York, London, Boston, Miami, New Orleans, Mumbai, Guangzhou and Shenzhen in China and Nagoya, Japan will be among the first to go.

Runaway climate change may eventually mean that the Earth's climate moves closer to that of Venus, with a surface temperature approaching the boiling point of water, but emerging worst-case consensus estimates for the 21st century add only about 30 degrees to the average daily temperature in most of the world and perhaps double that at the poles. Of course, as everyone knows, it's not the heat, it's the humidity. During the summer of 2015, we have already seen record heat index numbers over 150 degrees in parts of Iran.

If these dire scenarios start to materialize over the next few years, all the pesticides and advanced grain hybridization techniques of the Green Revolution will be rendered useless. While colonizing the moon or Mars at one time seemed like a very nice idea, the technology to move 7-10 billion people to such unlikely safe havens does not currently exist. Even getting one percent of the U.S. population to another cosmic home is a task that would defeat the best efforts of Edison, Tesla, Einstein, Newton and the entire Caltech and MIT faculties combined.

Although there are differences over whether the greatest threat to our way of life is abortion, gay marriage, racism or political correctness, most Americans recognize that there has always been a sword of Damocles hanging over our heads. We are the greatest country on Earth, the Dionysius of

nations, the world's policeman. Whether your chief fear is nuclear annihilation, the slow heat death of civilization, or the long-term consequences of
Obamacare, the cure is the same as the one Damocles took: take whatever
steps you can to return to a simpler, humbler, freer life. Live up to your responsibilities as a human being. Raise active and intellectually curious children. Avoid daily gallons of strong drink and massive doses of heroin or
Cialis. Take care of your property and live according to the Golden Rule.

Regarding the medical/insurance industrial complex, regard it as part
of the Human Comedy, not as the arbiter and enabler of your existence
on this planet. Doctors are as fallible and subject to pecuniary motivations
as the real estate brokers and used car dealers we are used to treating with
such great suspicion. A lot of what doctors offer you is ultimately the result of pressure from drug companies and medical device manufacturers.

An apple a day may not be enough to keep the doctor away, but if we
combine an organic, non-GMO apple with clean- sodium fluoride-free
water, a good work ethic, healthy sleeping habits, a vigorous and fulfilling
romantic life, disciplined study habits, an active social life, virtues such as
thrift and common sense, a solid hour or so of aerobic exercise, and plenty
of non-GMO green, leafy vegetables, I think we will be on the right track
to confront the challenges ahead in the best possible frame of mind.

Fifteen

The Accidental Drug Addict

"We are governed, our minds are molded, our tastes formed,
our ideas suggested, largely by men we have never heard of."

— *EDWARD BERNAYS*

There is no such thing as an accidental drug addict. Before you get upset with this statement, hear me out. The fact is, every single drug addict initially made a conscious *"choice"* to use the drug they have become addicted to. No one put a gun to their head and forced them to take the drug against their will; it was completely their decision to use or not to use. Since *"choice"* is the facilitating factor, the claim that someone became a drug addict by accident is simply untrue. If that is a fact, then drug addiction must no longer be classified as a disease, but rather an *"acquired condition."*

Ever since the age they could understand, I have taught my kids "The best drug dealer in the neighborhood always gives you the first hit for free." You can't blame him/her; it only makes for good business. It is your *"choice"* whether or not to take that first hit. It does not matter if the drugs you are offered are free or not, or if they are readily available; it is you and

123

you alone, who determines whether or not drugs of any kind end up in your body. Your Choice represents Your Power. You must clearly understand this point and never make a choice lightly. Addiction, in all forms, is slavery.

As parents, my wife and I made it our business to ensure that our kids clearly understood that when it came to the use of any type of drugs, they had only one true choice...the first choice, that's all. Teaching them, that unfortunately, everything after that first choice quickly becomes a *"need"* and no longer a *"want;"* the body becomes chemically addicted to the poison.

These days, both street drugs and Big Pharma drugs are created as such powerfully addictive biochemical compounds, that they begin to send the body into a cycle of physiological addiction shortly after their first use. The objective of any good drug dealer is to create a life-long customer; it's merely business, nothing personal. Users can easily become slaves; once they are biochemically addicted to a drug, any future choice is no longer a *"choice,"* it becomes a *"need."* Once this occurs, a new life-long customer is created. As a result, their former self is destroyed and their family is left asking the question, "what happened?" Sadly, this scenario occurs much too frequently in the United States with both prescription and street drugs. The scary fact is this is not an accident by either Big Pharma or the street dealer, but rather by design.

So, what is it exactly that influences ones choice to use or not to use; every person is different, so do we really know? Strong influences can be a person's upbringing, peer pressure, rebellion, insecurity or institutionalized social conditioning through the mass media that gives the illusion that drugs make you feel better and take care of the physical or emotional pain you may be experiencing. Let us explore the last influence, as Big Pharma drug ads are all over the TV and radio these days.

This type of drug advertising is direct and subconscious behavior based. As a result of the nonstop efforts made by the Rockefeller controlled Drug Trust, the public blindly accepts the institutionalized social conditioning made by mass media that drugs are always the answer; drugs make you feel good and drugs take away any form of pain you may be experiencing. No wonder Americans consume the most drugs of any country in the world. What do we get in return? Not better health, but rather more sickness.

The last thing on Earth any parent wants to see is their child in pain. From a child's early age, parents do exactly what they have been indoctrinated to do when their child expresses any type of pain, they medicate him or her (i.e. they give drugs). The use of drugs for pain has been deliberately conditioned into the minds of parents by the Allopathic Medical Monopoly and the Drug Trust since the early 1900's.

Remember, they are an industry; their job is to make money by creating customers, not cures. From a business model perspective, their purpose is to manage symptoms, not address the causes of the disease; there is no money in that. Since parents don't know what they don't know, they act in a manner that they have been conditioned to, by their own parents. So when a certain situation arises, they do not think, they simply react and do what was done to them. When it comes to managing any type of pain in a child, the first thing most parents are conditioned to do is to reach for, and administer a drug.

It is not by accident that so-called "medicine cabinets" are found in the bathroom of every house in the United States. These medicine cabinets serve as subconscious reminders to parents that drugs are always the treatment of choice. As a result, a child grows up learning from both of his or her parents that if, "something hurts" you quickly reach for a drug to take care of the problem. This type of conditioning in childhood can lead to some dire consequences later on in that child's life.

In the United States the average child grows up learning, *"For a headache - take this drug, for a stomach ache - take this drug, for a back ache - take this drug, to feel good - take this drug."* As they grow up, this thought pattern becomes imprinted in both the child's conscious and subconscious mind. The association that drugs are the answer if you just don't "feel good" becomes a well-established and accepted habit imprinted in a child's life, especially as they reach their school age years.

Young children learn very quickly and establish behavior patterns that are not only taught, but viewed. Mom and Dad's unknowing approval of drug use, can inadvertently establish a child's early acceptance of the, *"drugs make me feel better"* concept. This type of first "learned at home" concept has the power to destroy any child's future. As I stated earlier, "People have only one choice when it comes to any drug use; the first choice. Everything after that, quickly becomes a biochemical need, instead of a mental want. There are no accidental drug addicts, because every single drug addict executed their own free will of choice; unfortunately they chose to use."

Experts and parents tend to agree, the teenage years of life are the most stressful and most challenging years for any child. Statistics indicate, that this is also the time kids begin to experiment with recreational drugs, such as tobacco, alcohol, pot, heroin, meth, LSD, Ecstasy, mushrooms, etc. Could it be that since a child learns to suppress their physical pain with a drug since childhood and now face an "emotional pain" situation brought about by simply growing up, they may have a greater tendency to reach for the same type of remedy? A drug that they believe might help ease their emotional pain and make them *"feel good;* why not; it seems logical because drugs worked quite well for their physical pain.

126

Growing up is tough and teenagers go through a lot of emotional pain and self-doubt stemming from wanting to fit in, wanting to be liked, wanting to be cool or just wanting to be the life of the party. Acceptance by your peers is a natural human desire. In a teenager's mind, lines are easily blurred between the use of prescription drugs and recreational drugs. When drugs become the socially conditioned "right answer" to dealing with physical and emotional pain, it becomes very difficult for any teenager to "choose not to use." The most important thing every parent must understand is that no matter what the situation, every teenager carries within them their own power of choice.

Ultimately, it's not the drugs or their accessibility that is the problem facing the United States today; it is the social conditioning by the mass media that gives adults and children the illusion that drug use is the answer to all of their physical and emotional pain. Until this changes, drug addiction will continue to rise, more families will be destroyed and drug dealers of all kinds will continue to profit. It does not have to be this way; our children deserve better. Perspective is the first step towards prevention. I hope I've changed yours?

Sixteen

"Never be afraid to dare."
— **Vladimir Horowitz**

"Physical culture and nutrition is the salvation of America."
—**Jack LaLanne**

"Genius is one percent inspiration and ninety-nine percent perspiration." / *"Genius is one percent talent and ninety-nine percent hard work."* / *"Talent is a wonderful thing, but it won't carry a quitter."* / *"Talent hits a target no one else can hit. Genius hits a target no one else can see."* / *"Every talent must unfold itself in fighting."* / *"Talent is useful, but always keep your dagger sharp."* / *"How do you get to Carnegie Hall?" "Practice, practice, practice."*

— THOMAS EDISON / ALBERT EINSTEIN / STEPHEN KING / ARTHUR SCHOPENHAUER / FRIEDRICH NIETZSCHE / AMANDA QUICK / JACK BENNY? ARTHUR RUBINSTEIN? JASCHA HEIFETZ?

More than any other activity human beings undertake, gymnastic exercises show off the *joie de vivre* and utter fearlessness that should characterize perfect physical health. Not being able to do a cartwheel, a back flip, a triple somersault, or a one-handed hand-stand while twirling a baton is akin to not being able to achieve an erection, not being able to get out of bed, or not being able to find a job.

Most of us who watch the Olympics will agree that the most powerful sight in the world is a nubile young girl doing gymnastics. Who can forget the glorious, triumphant moments in the 1976 Montreal Summer Games, when Nadia Comaneci scored the first perfect 10s in sports history?

Even though no one before or since Nadia has achieved such a string of athletic perfection (although Secretariat came close), history does not stand still. It is instructive to watch back-to-back videos of women's horse vaults from the 1936 Olympics and footage of the same event in the London 2012 Games. In outtakes from Leni Riefenstahl's great film *Olympia,* we see *zaftig* figures in full-figured granny bathing suits who look like they stepped into the world from a Rubens painting all but plop over the vault. If the vault had been a real horse, that horse might have buckled under the strain. The judges would have had to borrow the relay gun to put the poor animal to sleep. Fast-forward to London, and you will see lithe, muscular young women who do double flips with various twists and turns built into the motion. Fifty years from now, if civilization as we know it lasts that long and Olympic Games are still of interest to our descendants, billions of armchair sports fans will gasp at the ineptness of our current champions.

Your health depends on flexibility and adaptability. We all know how important it is to keep mentally active as we grow older, but few of us retain the physical stamina and mental determination necessary to achieve great feats of strength, endurance and agility as the aging process overcomes will and way.

One of the reasons we fail to achieve super-human feats is that we give in too easily to grandma's advice to stay still, don't speak unless spoken to, never talk to strangers, don't swim for at least an hour after eating, put a hat on or you'll catch pneumonia, don't stay up reading. That and similar advice, internalized in childhood, is reinforced and expanded as the social control system gets its grip on us. Many of us live by rules that guarantee we will never amount to anything. The beauty of life is that we have the ability to change that destiny by adopting better habits at any time.

Jack LaLanne, who was a "sugarholic junk food junkie" as a teenager, found diet and fitness religion at age 15 and never looked back. He started sneaking off to lift weights and eat raw vegetables and whole grains. The new routine paid off handsomely, as LaLanne became America's first TV exercise guru, inspiring millions of people to start their mornings with calisthenics and a glass of carrot juice. He famously performed a legendary series of "escapes" from Alcatraz, swimming handcuffed and shackled through shark-infested waters. When he was well into his fifties, LaLanne beat 21-year-old Arnold Schwarzenegger in a fitness contest. To mark his 70th birthday, LaLanne used a rope held in his teeth to tow 70 boats (some with passengers!) for a mile.

Other great paragons of physical prowess may not have achieved Jack LaLanne's record of 96 happy years on Earth, but the exuberant employment of human energy to achieve artistic, scientific and sports milestones is what adds life to our years. Watching a great high school, college or pro quarterback carry his team to victory should inspire us not only to make bets on the next game, but also, and far more importantly, to practice throwing the football around with our children and buddies, to test and improve our agility, and to exercise and develop leadership skills in our daily lives.

Great dancers such as Rudolph Nureyev, Mikhail Baryshnikov, Misty Copeland, Fred Astaire, Ginger Rogers, Gene Kelly, Michael Jackson (and probably Bacchus back in the day) move us to tears with the beauty and excitement of their work. It is an intense pleasure to watch the physical comedy of Charlie Chaplin, Robin Williams, Roberto Benigni, Laurel and Hardy and Harold Lloyd. We thrill to the agility, power, and concentration of athletes such as Michael Jordan, Muhammad Ali, Bruce/Caitlyn Jenner, Serena Williams, Jesse Owens, Jim Thorpe, Shaquille O'Neal, Tom Brady, Usain Bolt, Michael Phelps, Derek Jeter, Cristiano Ronaldo, Pele, Tiger Woods, Jack Nicklaus, and the great Ronda Rousey.

While it is certainly no crime to enjoy the vicarious and sometimes even patriotic rush of sports fandom, this does not mean that we should abandon the field, the pool, the chessboard, the pitch, or the political arena to those who are clearly our betters, or who at least proclaim themselves "the greatest." All of these immortals – Babe Ruth included – were and are mortal men and women. Instead of throwing up our hands and having another beer, we should adopt the attitude of the YouTube squirrel that attacked and defeated a giant snake. Let Derek Jeter be your guiding light, but train your own body to adapt and overcome tough challenges. Don't just watch *Dancing with the Stars*, do some fancy footwork yourself!

Vigorous physical exercise is important for everyone. It will make you sleep better, improve your appetite, and may even make you a better lover. Cindy Crawford, a forceful advocate of exercise and fitness, once told an interviewer that she was doing Kegels (exercises involving pelvic contractions) as she sat for questions. Bank tellers, insurance agents and stay-at-home dads or moms probably need to do more than Kegel exercises to maintain their ability to endure long hours of drudgery, but even the dullest lifestyle can be transformed by the addition of a high-powered physical routine. John Gotti spent the last few years of his life staring at four concrete walls 24 hours a day, but he never gave in to his suffocating environment. He made it his business to do 2,000 stomach crunches every day. How much more could those of us on the outside accomplish with a little of his determination?

One of the most addictive viral videos online shows the exploits of "Russian Spiderman," who jumps and somersaults over building roofs, climbs up and over walls, and does so many impossible things in the course of ten minutes that millions of people worldwide have breathlessly watched his exploits over and over. Like Tony Hawk or Jackie Chan or the ubiquitous subway break dancers in New York City, Russian Spiderman turns the street magic hucksterism of everyday life in a poor neighborhood into an awesome display of power and beauty based on the miraculous flexibility of the trained human body.

Gary Null, who is one of the world's great broadcasters and a powerful spokesperson for compassion, fitness, natural foods and natural healing, has often described how his persistence rather than his natural gifts kept him on the path to excellence. Whether in race-walking or broadcasting or in any other of his myriad endeavors, Null worked his way from last-place finishes and scathing reviews to the pinnacle of his many fields of endeavor by learning from his defeats and concentrating on how to improve his performance. In *Gary Null's Guide to a Joyful, Healthy Life,* one of his many wonderful best-selling and non-best-selling books, Null writes of a verbal confrontation with an AIDS patient, who told him that he couldn't adapt a natural food diet that might dramatically improve his health because he didn't have Null's money, and was therefore doomed to permanent malaise and weakness. Null calmly explained to him that it was not a matter of money, but of will, and that his own weekly food budget was actually not much different from his interlocutor's. One can only hope that the man took these words to heart and took a stab at transforming his life. It is never too late!

When Plato, got sick, he did gymnastics. So should we! The ancient Greeks recognized that disease is generally caused by toxicities or deficiencies of one kind or another, and that the best way to overcome the threat of disease is to keep the body in optimal condition, by frequent performance of pirouettes, martial arts, acrobatics and wild dancing. Even though we now recognize that germs, bacteria, carcinogens and viruses are important vectors of disease, against which all physical exertions may be in vain, it remains generally true that maintaining a sound body gives you a leg up against infection by boosting your resilience and thereby the strength of your immune system. Too much bed rest, on the other hand, may just leave you with a foggy mind and bed sores.

The human body is a self-healing, self-regulating organism. It adapts to its internal and external environment on a second-to-second basis through the nervous system. Since the brain lives in the skull and the spinal cord lives in the spine, the proper bio-mechanical function of the spine is essential for the optimal adaptability of the nervous system.

I understand that health is the expression of the body's ability to adapt to physical, chemical and mental stimuli. Symptoms are signals that the body is unable to adapt accordingly to a physical, chemical or mental stressor. Not all symptoms are bad, as they encourage corrective action or may be related to the body's elimination of toxins. Similarly, the fact that you are feeling well does not mean that you are healthy. People can go for years with high blood pressure or clogged arteries before it catches up to them.

The Medical System generally treats and manages symptoms only. Only recently has prevention become a regular component of a medical consultation. Natural practitioners take a different, more proactive approach. They nurture nature as they attempt to address the root causes of disease and try to effect permanent cures by helping their patients restore and extend the lost adaptability of their bodies. Lifestyle changes rather than chemical potions are the prescription of choice in my practice.

Two of my fundamental principles as a Doctor of Chiropractic is to understand that motion is life and that structure effects function. My goal is to provide my practice members with the best possible advice and care that will enable them to achieve their highest "Adaptability Factor," so they can participate vigorously in the best life has to offer. In my examination, I check the spine for any bio-mechanical dysfunction (i.e. vertebral subluxation.) If I find a weakness or distortion, I introduce a specific energy/force through an adjustment of that dysfunctional segment. What I do is not a manipulation, but rather a specific adjustment or "reset" of an impaired spinal segment that is causing interference with the vital electrical "Life-Force" communication pathway. This pathway consists of the brain, the spinal cord and all the nerves that control and coordinate all the structures and functions of the human body. The more freely the Electrical "Life-Force" Energy flows from the brain throughout the body, the greater the body's ability to adapt to its internal and external environment accordingly. The proper expression of that ability is what I call health.

The body heals from within. Bodybuilding is as essential as pouring the foundation or putting up the framework of a house. There is no outer force that can heal. A body that is neglected will fall apart like a house of cards. Many allopathic physicians tell their patients that exercise is an option, but not to worry, because drugs ("statins") are another option that might work for them. To them I say, "No, no, no!" If drugs were the key to health, shouldn't the people on the most drugs be the healthiest? The fact that they are more likely the sickest should lead you to be very wary about confiding your health to the tender mercies of the pill cabinet. Doctors of Chiropractic such as myself understand that optimal adaptability, not drugs, are the key to health. As a Chiropractor, I see my role as akin to that of a stage-setter. I set the adaptability stage by correcting any bio-mechanical spinal dysfunction I find and the body innately does the rest. My role is to nurture nature and to obey natural law. My purpose is to help practice members retain the ability to use their natural gifts and potential to their fullest. Remember...health is wealth.

Though regular intense physical exercise is an indispensable element of maintaining optimal health, "having backbone" does not refer exclusively to physical prowess. What we are born with is immaterial. What matters is what we do to develop our gifts and to meet the challenges that life inevitably strews in our path. Among my personal heroes is the actor Christopher Reeve, who went from Superman to paraplegic in an instant when he was thrown from his horse and landed on his head. The Superman strength he had nurtured when in full possession of his faculties translated into an active life, including an active sexual life, during the years when he was confined to a wheelchair. He wrote books and travelled around the country to raise money for spinal cord research. He never gave up hope that he would walk again, and though he never managed to achieve that dream, his efforts made possible developments that are paving the way for others in similar circumstances to regain their lost physical abilities.

Franklin D. Roosevelt and John F. Kennedy are two Presidents who struggled with disability. Neither of them presented an image of weakness to the public or allowed themselves to succumb to the limitations imposed upon them by their conditions.

Theodore Roosevelt, one of the most vigorous men who ever lived, set the standard for our image of the President as a young man in perfect health. Sadly, most of his successors have been debilitated by disease or mental deficiencies of one kind or another, but those moments of weakness vanish in the rush of history. While we cannot erase the stains of Teapot Dome, the trysts in the Oval Office and its adjacent closets and hallways, the Great Depression, the Vietnam and Iraq wars, Watergate, Jimmy Carter's battle with the rabbit in the rowboat, and Gerald Ford's stumbles down the steps of Air Force One, what we generally remember about our leaders is one long series of triumphs: George Washington crossing the Delaware, the Emancipation Proclamation, Eisenhower leading his Armies to victory, Reagan riding his horse, Nixon in China, Kennedy in Berlin, Obama in Kenya.

While there have certainly been a lot of ups and downs since the days of Roosevelt, it is a refreshing tendency that Presidents have been among the few Americans devoted to the importance of exercise as a stimulant to hard work. Harry Truman and Richard Nixon took brisk long walks in the mornings. Gerald Ford swam a mile or two a day. George Bush I parachuted out of airplanes every five years. George Bush II chopped wood, ran seven-minute miles and rode bikes with Wounded Warriors.

Michelle Obama has been one of our most powerful exercise and nutrition advocates in the White House. She pumps iron every day and shows off her powerful biceps in the sleeveless dresses she favors. She has set aside a large area of the White House lawn for gardening. She has inspired millions by appearing on dancing shows and engaging in exercise contests with Ellen DeGeneres. She cajoled her husband into quitting smoking.

Any debate about whether energy and vigor matter in Presidential politics was firmly quashed by the emergence of Donald Trump, who has called out the government for stupidity, incompetence and poor negotiating skills while lashing out at "terrible" Jeb Bush and Hillary Clinton for weakness and low energy levels. Trump's challenge, while it has its sideshow elements, is an important reminder that our country needs to be awakened from its stupor. We have given in to warmongers, insurance companies and the medical lobby for so long that we are in danger of forgetting what made our country great, and what represents the only chance we have of emerging from the mountains of debt, garbage and toxic chemicals that are poisoning our economy, our environment and our health: self-reliance, enterprise, self-development, and the drive to cultivate our gardens.

Whether we allow the insurance companies, the big banks, the utility companies, Microsoft, Apple, Facebook and Google to dominate the economy is no longer a matter of choice, as the Control System has its hooks deeply into the meat. Obamacare, with its emphasis on allopathic drug promotion, has embedded itself within the medical establishment and is here to stay. Even though I acknowledge these realities, I do not feel that I am Don Quixote tilting at windmills. What I hope I have demonstrated in this book is that the Romneycare/Hillarycare/Obamacare model is not the equivalent of a Unified Field Theory for the healthcare universe. There is still an important place for those of us who believe in the power of fresh air and sunshine over poison pills and suppositories, and we will not give in so easily. The times ahead are uncertain, but we are sustained by the hope that it is our patients, not theirs, who will take the Horse Vault and Balance Beam Golds in 2064.

Seventeen

You Are What You Eat

"Hunger is the best sauce."
— **Arthur Schopenhauer**

*"If you're afraid of butter, use cream...The only time to
eat diet food is when you're waiting for the steak to cook...
People who love to eat are always the best people."*
— **Julia Child**

*"My doctor told me I had to stop throwing intimate
dinners for four unless there are three other people."*
— **Orson Welles**

There is no event more American than an eating contest. Whether our
eyes are glued to "survivors" eating insect larvae, glamorous women
eating vanilla or chocolate ice cream, bake-offs, competitions to become
the next Top Chef, hot dog gluttons on the Fourth of July, or friendly
family challenge competitions to see who can lose the most weight by

Christmas, food is more important to more Americans than politics, literature, travel, sex and sports combined.

The world we have created is largely an artificial one, built on a sandy foundation of lies, hype, technological razzle-dazzle, drugs and oil. Science has given us many great gifts, foremost among these the ability to recognize how disastrously we've despoiled the environment and ruined our health to boot. On the other hand, many of science's most conspicuous (and profitable) gifts basically abet and accelerate these terrible trends.

The Rockefeller Foundation and related philanthropies have wiped out enough tropical diseases and re-fertilized enough fallow fields to guarantee (*pace* P.T. Barnum) that McDonald's gets a bunch of new future regular customers every minute. While not everyone can afford to eat at McDonald's every day, Monsanto, the United Fruit Company, Nabisco and Wal-Mart have combined forces to ensure that even the poorest people in the world have a plethora of seemingly wonderful options. When the Wonder bread runs out, we can reach for the cookies and cakes.

Just a generation ago, people in Russia could live fifty years without seeing a banana and people in Taiwan had apples once or twice a year to mark major holidays. Today, the only places where people endure serious famines or shortages are the Middle East during fasting periods and in war zones; North Korea; large swaths of Central and South America, Africa, Southeast Asia, and Southern Europe; land-locked regions such as Mongolia and Tibet; the India / Pakistan / Bangladesh / Afghanistan continuum; Western China; and the rural areas and inner cities of the United States. Even in these areas, most people know from personal experience what an apple is, and most people even in the poorest countries usually have enough rice or other staple grain to stave off intense hunger pangs.

We seem to live in a world of abundance. The shops are full of goods, there is a Starbucks within a day's drive from anywhere, and big butts outnumber small ones everywhere but on the fashion runways. Even in the pages of *Vogue*, plus-size women are starting to crowd out the Kate Moss look-alikes. Unfortunately, for all the fuel that's being shoved and guzzled down from American gullets to American guts, most of what we eat is garbage.

We have to learn to treat the grocery store more like a book store. Instead of loading up with romance novels, Newberry Award winning children's books, textbooks we will never read and random books with pretty covers, most of us come into Barnes & Noble or Amazon with a title or subject already in mind. While most books end up on a shelf somewhere, never to be seen again, the ones we cherish provide food for thought and carry us through life on a magic carpet. By the same token, I stipulate that any food is better than no food. Without food, a person will die within a couple of weeks. On the other hand, a steady diet of romance novels or sugar-coated donuts will quickly turn the brain to mush, even though the shell of a person remains.

Americans feel the need to eat even while they are reading, watching TV, exercising or dancing. Planet Fitness hands you a cereal bar with your towel; TV dinners have replaced real dinners in millions of American households; dance clubs, like casinos, feature a well-stocked bar and a happy hour smorgasbord; and food writers have done everything but include scratch and sniff versions of their cookbooks, memoirs and diet books. We are used to the idea of reading in Starbucks over coffee and sandwiches; at home, we prop up a book on a stand as we prepare dinner.

The food section of the bookstore is one of the fastest-growing. Much of it consists of new versions of classic Julia Child, Jacques Pepin, Frugal

Gourmet, Galloping Gourmet, and Suzanne Somers cookbooks. The New York Times and the Culinary Institute of America have created reams of coffee table books worthy to stand beside the Bible on any home bookshelf. There are memoirs and how-to books by celebrity chefs and food writers such as Anthony Bourdain, Ruth Reichl, Martha Stewart, Melissa Clark, and Emeril Lagasse. There are cookbooks from every region of the country and the world, some of them with facing page translations and malapropisms and typos that make preparing some exotic meals a much more challenging proposition than putting together an Ikea cabinet set or an Erector kit skyscraper. We learn to substitute for cilantro, and to take the sugar recommendation of a recipe with a grain of salt, but few of the thousands of recipes published every day find true advocates among home chefs. Aside from homemade pizza and certain pulled pork barbecue recipes, kids are not too impressed with Mom's newly-acquired summer chef skills. Back to school means back to Mac and cheese, PBJ, French fries, onion rings and the occasional taco on weekends.

Although most of the efforts to change the American diet in a positive way are doomed to failure, there are occasional bright spots. Efforts to limit the size of the Big Gulp, campaigns to change the way chickens are raised, forcing donut and pastry companies to take trans fats out of their recipes, banning excessive MSG from Chinese takeout menus, and the push for organic and non-GMO foods are just a few examples of movements that have the potential to save lives by improving the way some Americans eat.

The problem is that the goalposts on the playing field keep changing. For every victory banning a dangerous preservative or hormone, food companies and their lobbyists and food chemists invent myriad ways to keep the tomatoes bright shining red, to make sure watermelons and oranges and grapes don't contain seeds, to make cookies and sausage taste better and better while reducing the package size and the nutritional content thereof. Freeze-dried, concentrated, frozen, canned, genetically modified and adulterated foods now take up far more space on the shelves than anything our forebears would recognize as healthy food.

In an era when cyber-dating and online social networking have become common, and when robot sex surrogates are touted as the next big thing in human relationships, nothing is more disturbing than Americans' love affair with shitty food. It may be true, as pop astrophysicist Robert Jastrow famously maintained, that silicon-based life forms represent the next stage of evolution, but this does not mean that carbon-based human beings will be able to thrive on dirt and sand diets anytime soon.

People have been eating for many years, but never before in human history have they eaten so much garbage with such great pleasure. If evolution means anything, this should not represent the final stage. We can and must do better.

Now that science has delivered to us an ever-improving understanding of the past, we should utilize this knowledge to construct a better lifestyle and a better diet. How does the body use nutrients? What foods spurred the rapid development of early hominid brains? Where did we go wrong to the point that every visit to the refrigerator represents a possible cause of disease or death? Is there anything left at Wal-Mart (America's most popular grocery store) that is not designed and engineered to kill us with sweetness and saltiness?

About a year ago, I discovered a diet that has saved my life and that helped imbue me with the drive to write this book. For many years, I have known about Dr. Heinrich Otto Warburg's pioneering work on the connection between acidic food and cancer. In trying to put these sound principles into practice, I tried out a variety of dietary systems, but mostly wasted a lot of effort trying to maintain a balanced diet featuring generous servings of the four or five food groups that the government recommends.

My diet beauty contest crowned a clear winner, a contestant who started out as the darkest of dark horses. After taking away what useful lessons I could from all the "caveman," "holistic healing," "low-sodium," and traditional diets in circulation, I now swear by the much-maligned but very satisfying dietary system of "Dr." Sebi, a self-taught "healer" whose work I will describe in greater detail below, and who has based his diet on popularizations of Dr. Warburg's work and on personal experience based on adjusting dietary patterns according to what makes his patients and followers feel healthy and well.

I feel so much better since I started following a modified version of the Sebi system. Although Sebi recommends a strict vegan diet, I feel that the addition of meat is an important factor in a balanced diet, and that it makes no sense to forego a nutritious and readily available food source that has always been a vital ingredient in our meals. My family and friends took notice of my new energy, and some of them, along with patients who come to me for nutritional counseling, have enthusiastically adapted the same diet. Although it has been a bit of a struggle, I long ago realized that it is more important to cut things out of the diet based on secure principles of natural healing than to seek the omnivore's ideal of maximum variety. I am not complaining and do not miss any of the dietary ingredients I have renounced (well, maybe pizza). Even with all the restrictions Sebi's diet entails, there is plenty to savor.

While I knew that processed sugar and the whole dessert and breakfast cereal industry are pretty much out to poison us, I had no idea that so many other categories of food, whole cookbooks' and grocery stores' worth, were equally complicit in bringing us down. It came as a shock to me that even such a simple meal consisting of a salad and a diet soda is only to be recommended to those who want to hasten the approach of their final hour.

It is as hard for most people to give up good-tasting, stomach-filling, energy-boosting food as it is to abstain completely from sex, entertainment and sports. Going on a diet is just above self-flagellation on the list of life's guilty pleasures, but I have found that limiting food consumption and choosing properly at your local farmer's market are the first and most important steps to a better and healthier life.

In modern America, the grocery store, like the drug store, is basically a casino where the only game is Russian roulette. The cards are stacked against you the moment you decide to buy rather than to grow your food and raise your own livestock. Modern foods that contain questionable ingredients such as animal by-products and even animal feces, things like hamburgers, hotdogs and breakfast sausage, are scientifically engineered to taste better than almost anything the mind can imagine, and are the subject of advertising campaigns that feature sexy women, sexy men and sexy places. McDonald's and Burger King magically transform the lowly ground-beef hamburger into a kind of ersatz ambrosia by throwing in lots of salt and ketchup and mustard, plus a tiny pickle slice or two. For the Big Mac (or is it the Whopper?), they pull out all the stops and write a tune: "two all-beef patties, special sauce, lettuce, cheese, pickles, onions on a sesame seed bun." Basically, they are feeding you salt on top of salt on top of salt, with a little bit of salted processed meat and soft, spongy salted bread thrown in. Dogs love hamburgers because they are probably a cut above dog food, but there is no reason people should eat shit like this, aside from lack of the time, creativity and money required to make better choices in a world where bad choices are presented as the only choices.

Under Dr. Sebi's system, which I wholeheartedly endorse, it has been set forth that the following "health foods" and "staple foods" are so bad for you that eating them will sap your energy and all but ensure that you end up in a cancer ward or on a dialysis machine:

- *Garlic*, while it may have some use in keeping vampires at bay, is a very bad actor in the body. Garlic is an oxide of allyl. Among other dangers, garlic doesn't allow wounds to heal. It is very acidic, 3.3 on the pH level chart. It burns cells and destroys cells by weakening cell membranes.
- *Celery* - Celery has a very high concentration of inorganic salt, and should be avoided at all costs. (Not all salt is bad for you. Sea salt is organic and easily assimilated by the body).
- *Broccoli* - Broccoli has no nutritional value. George W. Bush was right to condemn it.
- *Carrot* - The carrot should not be eaten. It is a Dutch hybrid plant made from combining Queen Anne's Lace and wild yams. It is loaded with starch.
- *Rice* – Whether you prefer white rice, fried rice, sushi rice, Basmati rice or brown rice, your best bet is to avoid processed rice altogether. According to Sebi, processed rice contains cyanide and high levels of starch. Rice will compromise the mucous membrane, and it is also high on the glycemic index. Wild rice is natural and the only type that should be eaten.
- *Acid/Hybrid foods & herbs* - Comfrey, rose hips, Echinacea, golden seal, licorice stick (has 50 times more sugar than sugar itself, and contains glucuronic acid) peppermint, spearmint, comfrey, and aloe vera are all on Sebi's "no eat" list.
- *Cow's milk and beef* – Cow's milk is acidic, 6.0 on the pH level chart. A cow is a hybrid animal and its meat, meat by-products, milk, and milk-based products are not suitable for consumption by humans.

- *Starch* – Starchy foods include spaghetti (and all pasta generally), rice, beans, potatoes, and cane juice (has the highest concentration of starch). Starch is a binder. It is a chemical only found in man-made food or plants that have been genetically engineered. Nature left to its own devices does not produce food containing starch.

- *Corn and soybeans* are two more staple crops that have undergone genetic engineering (GMOs) and are therefore *verboten* under the Sebi system. Today, up to 90% of the corn and soybean crops within the United States are Genetically Modified Organisms. Soybeans were historically used as the base material to make plastics, and are not much better for you than eating plastic would be. Soy products such as edamame, tofu and soy are also better avoided. Soy is a complex starch (or inorganic silica) that creates sulfides within the body. These sulfides in turn eat up iron and oxygen, eventually causing anemia.

- *Cassava* – Dr. Sebi didn't absolve African food. Although it is one of the most popular African dishes, cassava is not natural and even contains a form of the poison cyanide, which directly effects a person's brain and the ability to think clearly.

Dr. Sebi's list of banned foods is constantly updated. As people find more and more harmful and downright dangerous things to consume, they are added to the reject list like the resumes of so many undocumented immigrants or repeat felony offenders. The foods of the future – synthetic chicken, vitamin-fortified jelly beans, seafood donuts, and soylent green cookies – are all destined for Dr. Sebi's Hall of Infamy.

One could take a list at Dr. Sebi's list of banned foods and say that it unfairly demonizes foods that the government and common sense say are healthy. On the other hand, it would be easy to look at the foods he recommends as healthy and find all kinds of problems with them. There will be those who say that my version of his diet is unethical because it includes meat. Others may say that there is too little on the list that actually tastes good, and that it would be better if someone improved their diet a little bit rather than going the whole hog, as the trouble to obtain all the Sebi-approved foods is not worth the marginal health benefits over an alternative diet such as a vegan or vegetarian diet; a Mediterranean diet; a high-protein or even a protein shake diet; or a simple practice of keeping track of portions and calories while abstaining from crap that is obviously bad for the body like soda, cheese Danishes and hot dogs.

To those who make such criticisms, my reply is that all roads lead to Rome. If you keep a steady focus on maintaining good health and eating in a way that will preserve and enhance your physical condition, we are talking the same language. My purpose here is not to convert you to a particular diet or to insist that everyone who eats differently than I do is doomed to instant or slow death. All I want to say is that the Sebi diet has been a godsend to me and to those in my circle with whom I have shared it. It may not be perfect, but it is based on principles that make sense to me given what I know as a nutrition counselor about how the body works. I feel better and perform better at work and in my family responsibilities. I think you will find yourself in agreement if you give this diet a fair chance. If you can find a better approach consistent with naturopathic health principles, I'm all ears.

Human beings today live very differently from our ancestors. Everything about our "plugged-in" lifestyle is completely unnatural, to the extent that good health is largely an accident. Our "fight or flight" responses have been diminished to the point where we are content merely to follow a regular pattern without much variation. The bodies we inherited from spear-wielding hunters of wooly mammoths and saber-tooth tigers are now getting 30 minutes of aerobic exercise max even in the best cases.

Instead of rising and going to bed in rough accordance with the patterns of the sun, many of us jump up to the sound of an alarm clock and fall asleep only after long hours staring at computer screens, television sets, phones, tablets and video games. Six hours of sleep cannot replace the twelve hours the cavemen got. Distracted and fatigued drivers kill more people on the highways each year than drunk drivers.

If you take a polar bear from the polar regions to the jungles of Africa or to the sands of Arabia, he will probably survive no longer than a beached whale. While it may take a few years before things reach that point for the average polar bear, the odds are not good that the species will survive the century. The polar bear's natural adaptability factors are quickly breaking down as the cold climate and the food necessary to the animal's survival disappear and are replaced with hotter temperatures and more nimble prey. While humans may appear to be far more adaptable to climate change, there are so many other stressors in our environment that we may outlive the polar bear just barely unless we start taking better care of ourselves.

The quickest way to better health is a better diet. We have to be stronger to meet the challenges ahead, and getting there from here will not be easy. To get stronger, we will need to eat foods that are known to boost the immune system, while staying away as much as possible from eating chemically-enhanced, genetically modified processed foods that can destroy us from within.

The concrete jungle is not a jungle, and synthetic or hybrid or adulterated foods are not foods fit for human consumption. People who eat these things (nearly all of us) suffer biochemical, physical and mental indignities that lay us low long before our life's work is done. Because of the way we live, and especially because of the way we eat, each generation is getting sicker than the last. To reverse these trends will require reconnection with the life-giving force of nature.

The first and most important step to nurturing nature and re-connecting is to understand what you eat and how it affects your body. Food directly affects human behavior; it affects a person physically, chemically and mentally. If you change a person's diet, you ultimately change their thinking. In changing the way people think, you ultimately change and save lives.

Modern society has brought about an abundance of artificial foods, contaminated water and polluted air. In the distant past, before the air and water were subjected to the harmful practices introduced by human civilization, the early hominids ate things that enhanced their mental and physical powers to the point that they rapidly gained power over the land and over all other creatures on Earth. Even into the early years of the twentieth century, long-established culinary traditions tended to focus on diets that consisted primarily of vitamin-rich organic fruits and vegetables, natural grains and wild game. While there were some questionable new arrivals to the table, notably Spam and instant coffee, people did not commonly eat a pile of Chicken McNuggets, a Snickers candy bar and a large sugar- and phosphoric acid-laced Coke for lunch until relatively recently.

The good news is that Wendy's and Wal-Mart have not been able yet to destroy all traces of what used to be known as food, which is now long overdue for a comeback. The first rule of proper nutrition is an easy one to understand, and a relatively easy one to follow. Forget about hybrids, GMOs, processed sugar. Throw that stuff in the garbage. Nature makes only alkaline foods, and alkaline foods are what we should eat.

The term "alkaline" refers to the pH scale (pH = potential for Hydrogen, a measurement of acidity or alkalinity; a measurement of the concentration of hydrogen ions in a substance). The pH scale of both food and human blood runs between 0 and 14; with 7 (think water) being neutral. The pH value of healthy human blood is 7.365. The lower the pH of a food, the more acidic it is. Any food with a pH above 7 is alkaline and natural. It may come as a surprise that some of the most acidic foods consumed today are navy, pinto and lima beans, white rice, sugar, corn, eggs, cow's milk, cheese, potatoes and cassava. This cumulative acidity breaks down the protective mucous membrane of every cell in the human body, exposing it to a state of disease.

Dr. Otto Heinrich Warburg, winner of the 1931 Nobel Prize for Physiology or Medicine, claimed to discover the root cause of cancer in 1923. According to Warburg, "cancerous tissues are acidic, whereas healthy tissues are alkaline. All forms of cancer have two basic conditions: acidosis and hypoxia (lack of oxygen)." Dr. Warburg went on to state, "Deprive a cell of 35% of its oxygen for 48 hours and it may become cancerous." In Warburg's opinion, "disease cannot live in an alkaline body."

Why did Warburg focus so strongly on the idea that nature can only express life in an alkaline state? The answer stems from the concept that the human body, which is made up of 102 minerals, is electric. The claim that the human body can best be understood as a manifestation of electromagnetism was presented trenchantly in 1985 by Dr. Robert O. Becker, M.D. and Gary Selden in their best-selling book, *The Body Electric*. To sustain and properly to nourish the electric body requires live, electric food (alkaline foods). Nourishment requires proper assimilation into the tissues. Proper assimilation requires that there be a chemical affinity between the food eaten and the receiving structure, i.e., the human body. To accomplish this task successfully, the food source best suited for eating must contain the so-called "triune of life," i.e., Carbon, Hydrogen and Oxygen. This C-H-O arrangement is a hallmark of alkaline plants.

Cavemen had no acidic foods in their diets. "Acidic foods" are man-made; they do not naturally occur in nature. Many of the man-made foods we eat, e.g., hybrid plants and meats, and GMOs (genetically modified organisms), are incompatible with the natural nutrition needs of human beings. Hybrid and GMO fruits, vegetables and grains contain starch; starch is a binder and acidic. It does not exist in natural plants. Only natural plants support and nourish the electric human body.

Hippocrates, the Father of Medicine stated, "Let food be thy medicine and medicine be thy food." He was 100% correct, since no artificial food existed at that time. The human body has not changed, but unfortunately our concept of food has evolved in such a way as to threaten food's nutritional content and medicinal value. Much of what eat routinely contributes to making us sick. In place of the life-giving fruits, vegetables, meats and herbs enjoyed by Hippocrates and his contemporaries, Big Food and Big Pharma provide us with time-release stink bombs that melt in our mouths and explode in our stomachs. Food has become the ultimate chemical weapon.

Just as Volkswagen knew very well that its "emissions-free vehicles" were among its biggest polluters, and just as RJR Reynolds knew years before the general public that smoking causes cancer, Big Food and Big Pharma are very aware of the information I have just shared with you regarding the dueling roles of acidic and alkaline foods inside the body. Natural alkaline foods react very differently in the body from these "weaponized" man-made foods. Natural foods nourish and heal; acidic foods harm and destroy the protective mucous membranes of all cells in the body, resulting in the build-up of mucous in our organs and tissues. If Dr. Warburg is right, acidic foods can also cause cancer.

Even though the cards are stacked against us, there are still things we can do to give us a fighting chance. You have the power to fight disease, but doing this successfully will require careful study of your options and great willpower. Hippocrates, whose access to chemical was severely limited, used herbs to cure many of the diseases of his time. We should not neglect or diminish the powerful role of natural foods and herbs in keeping our bodies healthy and strong and free of disease.

Eighteen

*"We are being led by very, very stupid people... Sorry losers
and haters, but my I.Q. is one of the highest—and you all
know it!...It doesn't really matter what [the media] write as
long as you've got a young and beautiful piece of ass."*

— **DONALD J. TRUMP**

"If you can't dazzle them with brilliance, baffle them with bullshit."

— **W.C. FIELDS**

Ben Carson has made clear his belief that many of the fundamental
principles of science are works of the devil. The Big Bang Theory is a
"fairy tale," and the misguided ravings of Charles Darwin were prompted
by "the Adversary." Other examples of idiotic nonsense perhaps include
the Periodic Table, the Second Law of Thermodynamics, and the vile al-
gebraic equations bequeathed to us by the same people who brought us
Sharia law, a system of justice that resulted in planes crashing into the
World Trade Center and savage terrorists chopping off the heads of aid

workers and journalists who happened to be in the wrong place at the wrong time.

While I would not go as far as Dr. Carson, I share to some degree Dr. Carson's sentiment that many of the dogmas of science have as much need for examination and revision as the revealed truths of religion. Dr. Carson may not have believed in his heart of hearts that surgeons should wash their hands before poking their instruments into a human brain, but he mostly obeyed the ridiculous hospital protocols, a practical decision that probably resulted in the survival of a higher percentage of his patients than would otherwise have been the case. In the same way, I believe that, while science has much to tell us, we can often learn as much from the mouth of babes as we can from the pandering political speeches of eminent neurosurgeons such as Dr. Carson or the ravings of supposedly brilliant businesspeople such as Donald Trump and Carly Fiorina.

During the course of my almost 20 year career as a Doctor of Chiropractic, I have learned that over-dependence on highfalutin anatomical references or carefully-phrased citations of medical journal articles serves more to confuse a patient than to gain her trust. For this reason, I tend to follow KISS ("Keep It Simple, Stupid!) rules, even and especially when I am well aware of the underlying medical controversies and debates that could undermine my arguments among those who produce, vet and disseminate government White Papers on health and nutrition.

If we have learned nothing else over the past half-century, we should by now be well aware that government-funded scientific institutions and government advisory boards in all areas shade the truth, often by blacking out or eliminating critical caveats in documents released to the public. That is why we will find out only 50 or 100 years from now what the government knew about JFK's assassination, what really happened at Roswell in 1947, and who were the driving forces in debasing the American diet to such an extent that we are facing a future of synthetic meat, perhaps blended with a little human flesh to add flavor.

There are many forces that conspire to shut up people like me. Even during the past year, with so much attention focused on the battles between the Black Lives Matter movement and the police, there has been a quiet but steady stream of disturbing articles about naturopathic physicians who died under suspicious circumstances. For all the material progress we have made as a society, things are not much different from the not-so-long-ago days when KKK lynch mobs, gay bashers, Know-Nothing immigrant bashers, vigilantes, rogue CIA, ATF and IRS agents, Mafioso's, SS men, the KGB, the Spanish Inquisition, and the duly-constituted authorities of Salem, Massachusetts used thumbscrews, racks, bullets, beatings, interrogations, gas chambers, trials by fire, ordeal or kangaroo court, and an abundance of other torture methods and killing techniques to make sure that dissidents and aliens were stamped out before their noxious heresies could gain a secure following among the populace.

Because I know the depths to which the Control System will go to stamp out dissent, I pay attention when I see that a healer has managed to take everything thrown at him and come out smiling. "Dr." Sebi, a world-renowned herbalist, was such a man. Sadly, he passed away in 2016. In my opinion, he was one of the greatest healers of our time. His diet advice, which changed my life for the better, has been proclaimed by others who know about his work as the key to overcoming pathologies such as AIDS, cancer, lupus, diabetes, sickle cell anemia, herpes, and many more.

Unlike Dr. Carson, Sebi didn't have the cachet of Yale University and Johns Hopkins Medical Center stamped on his forehead. His formal education didn't include even graduation from kindergarten, but Dr. Sebi is no dummy. Like Maxim Gorky, Dr. Sebi was a distinguished graduate of the School of Hard Knocks; he also held an endowed fellowship from the Rodney Dangerfield Institute of No Respect and a Scarecrow's Brain Medal from the College of Life Experience. Many who heard his speeches proclaimed him as the intellectual heir of generations of snake charmers, faith healers, dowsers, witch doctors and voodoo practitioners, but most people who have tried his products and adopted his diet principles have nothing but the highest praise for him.

Dr. Sebi's platitude-larded presentations would not be out of place at a Faith and Freedom Summit or an Eagle Forum. Listening to Dr. Sebi gives you a sense of *déjà vu*, as if your grandmother has returned from the Beyond to regale you with her lovely stories and bring you back to your childish faith in God. Despite all these seemingly insurmountable obstacles for members of our hyper-rationalized society, Dr. Sebi's diet advice is like Grandma's apple pie: it regularly beats all comers at the local county fair.

It will probably not surprise you by now to learn that Dr. Sebi (born Alfredo Bowman November 1933 - August 2016) learned much of what he shared about the healing power of nature at the feet of his grand-mother, "Mama Hay," who lived on the edge of the Honduran forest near an idyllic river. Growing up, the boy had plenty of exposure to birdsongs, butterflies, fresh fish and mushrooms. Despite this well-inculcated love of nature, young Alfredo was not very good at looking after his health. When he came to the United States as a young man, the future "Dr. Sebi" was in rough shape. He was quickly diagnosed with obesity, impotence, asthma and diabetes. Doctors couldn't or wouldn't do much for him. Fortunately, a visit to an herbal healer in Mexico set him on the path to overcome these conditions. Upon his eventual return to Honduras, Sebi established The URSHA institute for herbal healing, following which the success of his diet-based treatments has brought him worldwide acclaim.

In 1985, Dr. Sebi advertised his services as a healer in a New York newspaper; soon thereafter, he had attracted a flock of loyal customers. Inevitably, Sebi was hauled before a judge to answer charges including false advertising and practicing medicine without a license. There may indeed be no such thing as a miracle cure, but the outcome of the trial was enough to restore one's faith in God. After presenting a roster of 70 witnesses willing to testify to the healing power of his cures, Sebi was acquitted in 1988 of the charges against him. His disciples took that result as an exoneration, and he became more popular than ever. For a time, Sebi served as a nutrition counselor to Michael Jackson, whose joyful, athletic dancing under Dr. Sebi's care caused a quantum leap in his popularity, and whose unfortunate abandonment of a drug-free natural food regimen led to his untimely tragic death.

Big Pharma doesn't want you to hear of Sebi's cures, because his success undermines the fundamental principle that only the treatments and research studies of the allopath's have any valid claim to address the physical infirmities and diseases of our citizens. When you see phalanxes of lawyers and medical experts going after Sebi and others who preach similar doctrines about the healing power of herbs and diet to cure disease, you should never forget that it is your pain and suffering that keeps these establishment doctors and their CYA lawyers in business. Dr. Sebi's point of departure is his belief that the root cause of disease is mucus. This idea was introduced by German-born Professor Arnold Ehret (1866-1922), author of such books as *The Mucusless Diet Healing System, Rational Fasting* and *The Cause and Cure of Human Illness,* who was known for his advocacy of the benefits of fruitarianism and extended fasting. Ehret theorized that disease manifests itself in the body where mucus has accumulated, and concluded from this observation that disease only lives in an acidic environment. Drawing on this important work, Dr. Sebi formulated diet protocols including his trademarked African Bio-Mineral products and accompanying recommended nutritional changes. Sebi's products help cleanse the body by extracting mucus. They are intended to nourish the body by providing minerals and nutrients on a cellular level, thereby enhancing the body's natural ability to regenerate and heal. Dr. Sebi uses a nutritional guide that promotes an alkaline environment in the body to support the healing process and achieve optimal health.

The purpose of this book is to return the power of health and healing back to the people. It is our actions that change our situations. We may all currently be members of "Generation Sick," but it doesn't have to end that way. There is hope through learning how to nurture nature and reconnecting with the cosmic arrangement between man, the universe and the environment. Throughout our lives we all deserve to be healthy, happy, vital and strong. We should strive to die of old age, not disease.

To make better health choices, we need better information. I have done my best to give you a sense of what has worked for me and for my practice members. My goal is to enlighten as well as entertain my readers by pointing out the reasons why some of the life-saving information I have presented, including the wonderful Sebi diet, has been disparaged, discredited and covered up by the Control System and its puppet politicians and flacks. Due to Dr. Sebi's surprising and untimely death in August 2016 while in police custody in Honduras, some speculate that he may have been murdered to silence him and terminate his organic healing work. You are free to choose another path, as there is no unique or perfect way to health that works for all people at all times. Whatever you decide, I hope this book will prove to be a key milestone in your quest to develop a healthier, happier and better mode of life. Onward!

Nineteen

NATURAL HOPE: THE RE-CONNECTION

*"Life is pretty simple: You do some stuff. Most fails. Some works.
You do more of what works. If it works big, others quickly copy it.
Then you do something else. The trick is the doing something else."*

— *LEONARDO DA VINCI*

Leonardo da Vinci was one of the most versatile and adaptable human beings ever to grace the stage of life. Da Vinci was a major player in the revival of natural medicine and a pioneer of healthy living. He was repaid for his abstemious habits with a (relatively) long life and a vigorous old age.

Da Vinci's contributions to the field of nutrition include a machine to roast meat on a spit, but he is often cited as a pioneer of the vegan diet, based on cutting anti-meat comments put in his mouth by the Russian novelist Dmitri Merezhkovsky: *"Truly man is the king of beasts, for his brutality exceeds them. We live by the death of others. We are burial places! I have since an early age abjured the use of meat, and the time will come when men will look upon the murder of animals as they look upon the murder of man."*

Da Vinci's most famous monumental work is *The Last Supper*, a masterpiece where the greatest dramatic moment of the Gospel plays out at the supper table. Da Vinci's legacy serves as the guidepost for my (almost) *Last Chapter*, in which I ease up on the political commentary and invite you to take a seat at my humble table.

I hope that my arguments and my example will serve as a foundation you can build on as you pursue your own quest for a healthier, happier, better life. I hope that this book generates a vigorous debate that brings my errors to the surface and helps me grow by expanding my knowledge base and introducing me to interesting new thoughts and ways of life. I hope that the questions I raise about the legitimacy of our current healthcare system and food production practices will lead to long-overdue reforms that make the world a better place.

Encore #1: *"La Campanella"*

"Necessity is the mistress and guide of nature."

— **LEONARDO DA VINCI**

For many veteran concertgoers, the highlight of a performance is the few minutes devoted to encores at the end of the show. That's when the player relaxes and pours out the essence of his or her soul to the audience. Now that my argument, such as it is, has been safely delivered to the reader, I would like to provide a *bias* or two to leave you humming and shaking in your seat.

In every man's life, it is said, there comes a point where he recognizes the fact that he is "sick and tired of being sick and tired." This moment of recognition is commonly known as a mid-life crisis. The decline happens gradually, but at a certain point in time, the body begins to have a more difficult time cashing checks the mind has written. As our physical and mental powers start to show unmistakable signs of decline, we become aware of our own mortality. Thoughts of imminent or even eventual death have a way of focusing the mind on ways to stave it off.

My mid-life crisis occurred when I turned 40. I began to develop an overwhelming fear of the social stigma that getting older seemed to entail. When I was a kid, I saw people who were 40 as "fossils." Now that I had become one of these fossils, I realized that I was still 20 in my own mind. The only problem was that this 20-year-old me was trapped in a 40-year-old body that began to change, not for the better, with each passing day. I took extra time to get going, and my speed was barely enough to keep me at the back of the pack. As a life-long athlete, who truly enjoys participating in all aspects of the game of life, my new-found purpose in life was to find ways to keep my body physically, chemically and mentally sharp for as long as possible. My mid-life crisis marked the beginning of my personal journey in search of peak performance and optimal adaptability.

As a Doctor of Chiropractic for almost 20 years, I understood that health is "the expression of the body's ability to adapt to physical, chemical and mental stimuli accordingly." I also understood that the human body was electrical (according to science, we are considered alive when electrical activity in our brain is present) and that everything that is alive is in a constant state of motion and change. Cessation of motion and adaptability means death.

Compared with most other men my age, I was in pretty good shape at 44. I did not suffer from any diagnosed health problems, but I noticed that my energy level was down from what it had been just five or so years before. I had gained some weight, especially around the belly area. My joints were stiff in the morning and evening, even though I got adjusted by my chiropractor almost every week. My mind seemed cloudy at times; and my ability to adapt to physical, chemical and mental stressors had obviously become diminished. I was not sleeping well: it took me longer to get to sleep; I did not sleep soundly; and when I got up, I was still tired. This was the big red flag that made me realize that I was not going down the right path regarding my health. I have always said to my patients and clients, "Show me a person that does not sleep well, and I will show you a person who does not heal well." Most healing occurs while we are deep in REM sleep.

It suddenly became crystal-clear to me that I wasn't as healthy as I thought I was. I was a card-carrying member of Generation Sick, and time was running out for me rapidly. Rather than sitting back and watch the tumors grow and metastasize, I decided to take corrective action. As I tell my practice members, we are all responsible for our own health and well-being. "Doctor, heal thyself" became a personal motto rather than just a sign on my office entrance hall wall.

To increase your chances for success, to remain focused and stay motivated, it is always best to undertake and go down the difficult path of a new life journey with someone else, and the best travel companion is someone you love and who cares for you. My wife is the love of my life and my best friend. I've always told her, "You are no good to anyone else unless you take care of yourself first. That is not selfish, it is responsible." When I turned 44, my wife, who was 41, had already suffered from endometriosis and fibroids for a few years. The worst thing in the world is to see the person you care about most in severe pain. The feeling of helplessness is overwhelming. Since we were both "sick and tired of being sick and tired," we decided to take responsibility for our own health and to make the healing journey together.

As a Doctor of Chiropractic, I recognized the health issues and challenges we were both facing. I understood the fact that the human body was created as a self-healing, self-regulating organism. My job now was to learn exactly what it takes to keep the electrical body adapting to its internal and external environment at the highest level possible. Everything I had learned up until now from my studies at various colleges and universities, and at the feet of a succession of well-credentialed health and wellness experts, failed to produce the results my wife and I so desperately sought to achieve. Although I felt frustrated and helpless at times, my gut instinct told me, "seek and you shall find." I realized that I had to seek a different path to obtain a different result. This book, which sees the light in my 47th year, is the result of my search for healing.

Most of the central principles of life and natural law were first discovered and put into practice thousands of years ago by the Egyptians, the Greeks and the Sumerians. The human body has not changed since the time of Hippocrates. What held true then still holds true today. Even though we now live in a society that seems to be deliberately designed to allow us to ignore and even contravene the basic principles of human nature, we can still learn valuable lessons from people who were more in touch with nature.

Today, we have become disconnected from our natural environment and our cosmic arrangement with our universe. Even though this artificial world is all we have ever known, we are as out of place as Eskimos in the Sahara or pygmies in the tundra. Disconnection with nature makes a person sick, miserable and subject to continual suffering.

I was taught what to eat and what to drink by my parents who, despite their good intentions, were programmed what to feed me by the food industry and the medical establishment. Since the media propaganda positioned these industries as experts who knew best the needs of a growing child, why would my parents or your parents dare question anything?

As I dug deeper down the rabbit hole of health, what I discovered was that the simplest and most vital thing any person can do to protect their well-being is to understand what exactly they should eat and what they shouldn't. This advice sounds simple, but it is very hard to put into effect in the world we now inhabit.

Encore #2: "The Minute Waltz" (or "Recapitulation")

"If you want to be healthy observe this regime.
Do not eat when you have no appetite and dine lightly,
Chew well, and whatever you take into you
Should be well-cooked and of simple ingredients.
He who takes medicine is ill advised
Beware anger and avoid stuffy air.
Stay standing a while when you get up from a meal.
Make sure you do not sleep at midday.
Let your wine be mixed with water, take little at a time
Not between meals, nor on an empty stomach.
Neither delay nor prolong your visit to the toilet.
If you take exercise, let it not be too strenuous.
Do not lie with your stomach upward and your head
Downward. Be well covered at night,
And rest your head and keep your mind cheerful.
Avoid wantonness and keep to this diet."

— **Leonardo da Vinci**, *1515 (reprinted from Dave Dewitt's* Da Vinci's Kitchen: A Secret History of Italian Cuisine*)*

The human body is electric, and requires "electric" food to provide nourishment. Nourishing is very different than feeding. Feeding requires nothing but eating. You can eat anything and feed the body. That is not the same as nourishing the body, any more than having a relationship with your left hand or a sex toy is equivalent to sharing your life with a fellow human being.

Once I discovered that the body was an electromagnetic organism that required alkaline foods and needed to be nourished instead of fed, my entire perspective changed. At that moment I saw that the glass that I was told was half-empty, was also half-full. I immediately began to think twice about what I chose to eat. Prior to that epiphany, I did not realize that there were such things as acidic and alkaline foods. I just knew what most of us are told about eating: "Fat was bad, carbs were no good, and sweets should be limited." With my new, better-informed perspective, I began to understand that food directly affects human behavior. A person who changes his diet to include more alkaline foods and less acidic foods will soon discover that not only his body, but also his cognitive processes are much improved. I recalled the famous saying of Hippocrates, "Let food be thy medicine, let medicine be they food." I then made the leap to the conclusion that what he was referring to was eating natural alkaline foods. In his day and age, there was no such thing as man-made foods like the hybrids and genetically modified organisms (GMOs) we have in our grocery stores today.

If alkaline foods were good enough for Hippocrates, I thought they should be good enough for me and my wife. Slowly changing my eating plan to include more organic alkaline foods was the first and most important thing I did on my journey to improve my health and well-being. The effects were amazing. My energy increased and my sleeping improved. I was stronger when I worked out at the gym, and my joints weren't as stiff.

I even lost eight pounds of body fat in approximately six weeks, without even trying. My wife lost over 16 pounds in eight weeks and her female issues improved dramatically. These amazing health results led me to investigate the backwater issue of alkaline vs acidic foods more closely. What I discovered supported my understanding that the body becomes sick because of either "deficiency or toxicity" of one form or another. Based upon the impressive personal results that my wife and I achieved through simply making different food choices, I reached the obvious conclusion that food plays a fundamental direct role in the development of both the deficiencies and toxicities in our bodies.

Alkaline foods are rich in vitamins and minerals. Unfortunately, we have been conditioned by the Big Food industry to eat foods deficient in minerals and abundant in traces of the ubiquitous pesticides and chemicals that now saturate our food, our water, and our soil. We have been sold a bill of goods that makes us the most over-fed and under-nourished society in history.

After consuming any food, the first place that reaction occurs is within the central nervous system (i.e., the brain and spinal cord). Deficiencies (of any of the 102 basic minerals required for optimal body functioning) and toxicities (from any poison), lay the foundation for the expression of dysfunction and disease within the human body by reducing the body's ability to adapt to its internal and external environment as it should.

Acidic foods do not assimilate into the cells of the body. They try, but the body rejects them continuously. Think of it as someone is trying to get into your house, but you don't want to let them in. They continue to knock continuously, without ever stopping. They knock at the same spot of the door, every day, all day, for weeks, months and even years. As a result, the one spot they knock on continuously begins to erode away. The door begins to develop a mark and even an imprint on the exact spot where the person has been knocking all that time. Eventually, that door becomes pitted and erosion of the outside material persists until the door begins to thin, weaken and fade. That door is never the same. It becomes damaged and weathered over time from all the knocking. Eventually, you are left with no choice but to replace the door. A wiser choice would be to remove or send away the person who is continuously knocking at the door.

The door represents the membrane of every cell within your body. The person continuously knocking at your door represents acidic food. The damage on the door represent the injury done to the cell by the acidic food trying so hard to get in. The end result is that the cell membrane becomes compromised because of the constant irritation. In response to this distress signal, the cell is in a constant state of injury and repair. As the membrane of the cell continues to erode, its defense mechanism becomes compromised. This allows for various toxins to enter the cell, toxins that otherwise wouldn't be able to get in. The human cell is programmed to survive and adapt to its environment. As a result of being in a constant state of injury, the cell has to fight desperately to maintain itself in existence. It does this by producing mucus throughout the injured membrane. This mucus accumulates over time and traps within it the toxins that are drawn to the area of the cell. Eventually, the mucus accumulates around the cells, which makes up the tissues, which makes up the organ affected, which then affects the system of which that organ is a part, and eventually affects the health and adaptability factor of the entire human body. Everything is connected. You cannot affect one cell without potentially affecting the entire human organism.

This is the battle that rages every day within your body, simply because of the foods you have chosen to eat. Removing the irritation to the cellular membrane reduces the inflammation of the cell, which in turn, reduces the mucus produced by the cell and supports a healthy generative cellular environment, as opposed to the degenerative environment that medical experts today call "inflammation," and that often leads to an "itis" of some kind. "Itis" in such words as "arthritis" simply mean "inflammation of," as in, "inflammation of a joint is called arthritis."

My research about the effects of acidic foods on cellular membranes led me to the works of two self-proclaimed healers who had also come to understand the cellular membrane, acidity and mucus connection. That, in a nutshell, was the genesis of this book.

Encore #3: "Food, Glorious Food!"

"Nothing strengthens authority so much as silence."
— LEONARDO DA VINCI

So what should we eat to help nurture nature and support the alkaline state of the electric human body? I will gladly share with you what I and my family have chosen to include and eliminate from our eating plan. The changes we chose to make were slow and minor at first, but made a tremendous difference in the way we function mentally, physically and chemically.

The first step I took was to eliminate from my diet as many hybrid foods as possible. Hybrid foods are foods that do not grow in nature, but could be called "man-made." Specifically, this term covers crossbred foods that must be nurtured and protected by humans, because otherwise they would be overcome by birds, insects, worms, fungi and bacteria. They cannot sustain themselves and adapt to the environment on their own. Examples of common hybrid fruits are: seedless apples, several date varieties like kiwis, seedless pineapples, seedless citrus fruit, seedless grapes, seedless persimmons, and seedless watermelons. Common hybrid vegetables include beets, carrots, corn, potatoes, celery, and cauliflower. Common hybrid nuts, seeds and beans include cashews, oats, rice, wheat, wheat grass, soy, legumes, and most beans. Common hybrid herbs include goldenseal, ginseng, echinacea, dong quai, aloe vera, nutmeg, comfrey and garlic.

Nearly all of the hybrids listed above are included in our daily modern diet. There is therefore no cause for wonder that we live in a sick, suffering and malnourished society. It is a simple matter of garbage in, garbage out.

All hybrid foods are acidic. They have to be because their molecular structure is incomplete. As a result, they are high in both sugar and starch. They are not assimilated into the cells as nourishment in the same way as natural, wild and native foods are. Hybrid foods are devoid of proper mineral balance that all wild foods contain. Remember, the body is made up of 102 minerals. When we eat a lot of hybrid fruits and vegetables that do not possess the proper chemical affinities, these are not easily assimilated within the cell. This leads to mineral deficiencies. That causes the body to leech heavy minerals from the bones and bring these heavy minerals into the blood to buffer the sugar and the starch. The hybrid sugar, when consumed, is not properly recognized by the liver and pancreas. That causes those organs to stress. Since the minerals and sugars from the hybrid food are not assimilated into the cell, they are spilled off into the urine and excreted by the body. The irritation and increased stress of the liver and pancreas by the consumption of hybrid sweet fruits and starchy vegetables can cause mineral loss and a build-up of toxicity within the body. This sets the stage for sickness and disease.

Since hybrid foods are not designed to be consumed by the organic body, they do not assimilate into the cells completely and instead are stored as toxins. As a result, they irritate the membrane of every cell in the body and eventually cause damage to the mucus membranes. That compromises the integrity and function of the cell as a whole, as well as the cell's function as part of an organ, structure and/or system of the human body. Hybrid foods are known to feed fungal and yeast conditions like Candida, whereas non-hybrid, natural or wild fruits and vegetable are not associated with such pathologic conditions.

Natural food advocates have estimated that approximately 99% of the foods available in the United States of America today, thanks to the Big Food Industry, are hybrid in creation and are high in starch and sugar. Many carry traces of cyanide poison within them. Half of these food categories are so dangerous that I listed them as foods to avoid in my discussion of the Sebi diet. If that "Common Food Alert List" makes one mother have second thoughts about what she puts in her grocery cart, this alone makes all the effort of writing this book worthwhile. If a single cell is important, just imagine the power of a single mother!

At the end of this section, for informational purposes only, is a list of foods that are alkaline, non-hybrid and that are easily assimilated by the body, resulting in proper nourishment. Dr. Sebi uses this list with his clients; and Professor Arnold Ehret had many of these foods included on his list as well. Even though some of these items are quite difficult to find and relatively expensive, my family and I have chosen to incorporate as many of these foods into our daily eating plan as possible, and we have found that adopting this diet was the best thing we could have done. Our kids initially found it tough to do without a lot of the junk food their peers eat, but they have become outspoken diet evangelists as the benefits of the switch became obvious to all of us. As Colleen and Bryant and Conor spread the word, Vic's Buffalo Grill is becoming an increasingly popular gathering spot for newbie neighborhood healthy eating aficionados.

Important note: Both Dr. Sebi and Professor Ehret advocate an alkaline, vegan, plant-based diet. I choose to differ with them to the extent that I add bison meat to my diet. The North American bison was hunted nearly to extinction by the pioneer settlers of the West. In recent years, Ted Turner, the founder of CNN and the force behind "a one-man quest to save the world," has bought up enough land in Montana and other Western states – over two million acres – to become the second-largest individual landowner in the United States. Turner has set aside much of this land as grazing area for bison herds. He has been trying to promote bison meat as a healthier alternative to beef cattle, and his arguments and his cause resounded with me. The North American bison is a natural, non-hybrid animal, and short of abandoning the country to Native Americans, restocking the Western grazing lands and national parks with bison is perhaps the single most viable thing we can do to restore the country to some of its original owners.

My grandmother had it right: "Never use a microwave, it kills your food!" Now let's eat!

ALKALINE, NON-HYBRID FOODS LIST

Vegetables

- Amaranth greens – same as Callaloo, a variety of spinach
- Avocado
- Bell Peppers
- Chayote (Mexican squash)
- Cucumber
- Dandelion greens
- Garbanzo beans
- Green banana
- Izote – cactus flower/ cactus leaf – grows naturally in California
- Kale
- Lettuce (all, except iceberg)
- Mushrooms (all, except shiitake)
- Nopales – Mexican cactus

- Okra
- Olives
- Onions
- Poke salad – greens
- Sea Vegetables (wakame/dulse/arame/hijiki/nori)
- Squash
- Tomato – cherry and plum only
- Tomatillo
- Turnip greens
- Zucchini
- Watercress
- Purslane (Verdolaga)

Fruits ("No canned or seedless fruits")

- Apples
- Bananas – the smallest one or the Burro/mid-size (original banana)
- Berries – all varieties- elderberries in any form – no cranberries
- Cantaloupe
- Cherries
- Currants
- Dates
- Figs
- Grapes- seeded
- Limes (key limes preferred with seeds)
- Mango
- Melons- seeded
- Orange (Seville or sour preferred, difficult to find)
- Papayas
- Peaches
- Pear

- Plums
- Prickly Pear (Cactus Fruit)
- Prunes
- Raisins –seeded
- Soft Jelly Coconuts
- Soursops – (Latin or West Indian markets)
- Tamarind

Herbal Teas

- Allspice
- Anise
- Burdock
- Chamomile
- Elderberry
- Fennel
- Ginger
- Raspberry
- Tila

Spices and Seasonings

Mild Flavors

- Basil
- Bay leaf
- Cloves
- Dill
- Oregano
- Parsley
- Savory

- Sweet Basil
- Tarragon
- Thyme

Pungent and Spicy Flavors

- Achiote
- Cayenne/ African Bird Pepper
- Coriander (Cilantro)
- Onion Powder
- Habanero
- Sage

Salty Flavors

- Pure Sea Salt
- Powdered Granulated Seaweed (Kelp/Dulce/Nori – has "sea taste")

Sweet Flavors

- 100% Pure Agave Syrup – (from cactus)
- Date Sugar

Grains

- Amaranth
- Fonio
- Kamut
- Quinoa
- Rye

- Spelt
- Teff
- Wild Rice

Nuts and Seeds – (includes nut and seed butters)

- Hemp Seed
- Raw Sesame Seeds
- Raw Sesame Tahini Butter
- Walnuts
- Brazil Nuts
- Pine Nuts

Oils

- Olive Oil (Do not cook)
- Coconut Oil (Do not cook)
- Grapeseed Oil
- Sesame Oil
- Hempseed Oil
- Avocado Oil

Encore #4: "Happy Birthday, Mr. President"

Intellectual passion drives out sensuality.

— *Leonardo da Vinci*

*Marriage is like putting your hand into a bag of
snakes in the hope of pulling out an eel.*

— *Leonardo da Vinci*

We aren't necessarily getting the nutritional value that we need.
So as I analyzed all those things, I began to realize that that
was a significant portion of my problem. And I started to
try to figure out, how do you get that supplementation? Well,
I became particularly interested in glycoscience, glyconutrients.
These things are in your apples, your bananas and beets and
everything, you know, that's growing, but by the time we get
them, they frequently are gone. And I discovered you can actually
concentrate those in powders and pills and things like that. And
there are a number of different types of vitamins and supplements
that are there. I advise people to actually look into this.

— BEN CARSON

The Trump administration has the potential to be the sexiest in history, but is more likely than not to be the least sexy. Most of the competent candidates that ran against him seem to suffer from the usual geriatric complaints: flaccid muscles, sagging pectorals, pronounced turkey necks, bad hearing, poor eyesight, low T, low E, forgetfulness, and serious dental hygiene problems. The incompetent candidates, many of whose parts are in better working order than their more experienced colleagues, have the charisma of gnats and the sex drives of potted plants. This may explain why American public elected Trump?

There is no American leader on the immediate horizon who could hold a candle to JFK or even Ronald Reagan. Indeed, many Americans believe that the best way to solve the problem of the "dead wood" Presidency we have come to expect since George Bush I would be to replay pertinent Ronald Reagan or Bill Clinton speeches on national TV in response to every major crisis or national holiday. Instinctively, many of us believe that Ronald Reagan knew most of the answers and the proper soothing words for every situation our nation is likely to face in the next thousand years. Where Reagan fell a little short, Bill Clinton was strong. Ronald Reagan and Bill Clinton (mostly) kept us out of war and presided over periods of massive technological growth and widely-shared (or at least widely-publicized) prosperity.

The last thing we need at this time, as Barbara Bush wisely observed at the outset of the 2016 campaign, is another Bush or another Clinton. Fortunately, the Control System that has its greedy paws on the campaign finance system, the voter turnout and suppression operations, and the media access portals has rigged the game in such a way as to favor the election of Donald Trump.

Now that Donald Trump has made it to the top, the herb of choice for most Americans will be marijuana. His platform wanted to see it legalized in all 50 states. As a result, the Fourth of July barbecue will be a far more mellow affair, and Thanksgiving stuffing will send grandpa to the couch with a panic attack.

Dr. Ben Carson was the biggest wild card when it come to the tantalizing possibility of official government recognition of the potency and beneficial effects of medicinal herbs. Carson is a trained allopathic surgeon, but he also served for many years as a paid commercial spokesman for Mannatech, a Texas-based nutraceutical company whose "glyconutrient" products made demonstrably false and misleading claims that their signature drug Ambrotose could heal or mitigate "toxic shock syndrome, heart failure, asthma, arthritis, Lou Gehrig's Disease, Attention Deficit Disorder, lung inflammation, multiple sclerosis, and AIDS." Ambrotose supposedly also makes cancer disappear.

While I applaud Dr. Carson for having an open mind, particularly when large sums of cash pass into his pockets, I totally disagree with his premise that pharmaceutical conglomerates and nutraceutical fly-by-night companies have been able to distill all the active ingredients we credit for the beneficial healing effects of herbs into little pills that people can pop to cure cancer.

For the benefit of those who may know herbs only as a mix of seasonings that go into Shake-and-Bake chicken with the spices or as pills at the local GNC store, I would like to share the wonderful news that Dr. Carson is right to seek healing outside the traditional avenues of the pharmacy. Although I would not recommend (as he did) ingesting anything on the following list in pill or suppository form, I can verify from personal experience that the substances below are effective means of warding off and curing diseases. Learning what herb does what takes a lifetime of study, but that lifetime will likely be much longer if you incorporate some of these substances into your daily regime starting today.

Detoxification:

The following herbs have been noted to help support the removal of toxins, acids and mucus from the electric body: cascara sagrada, prodijiosa, rhubarb root.

Multi-Mineral Nourishment:

Irish sea moss, rich in minerals, has been noted to support the bones, thyroid and other glands, and to be effective in mitigating pulmonary illness, bad breath, respiratory issues, coughing and dysentery. It dissolves fat; is a natural diuretic; calms appetite; aids in digestion; prevents ulcers; regulates bowl movements; protects against obesity; supports skin health; and helps prevent kidney and heart disease. It is high in calcium and zinc.

Ortiga, bladderwrack, tila, nopal – These herbs are rich in minerals and chlorophyll. They help support the entire electric body through good nourishment. They also support the heart, brain, blood and central nervous system.

Energy and Revitalization:
Sapo, hombre grande, contribo, chaparral, valeriana and Irish sea moss - These herbs have been noted to energize, cleanse and revitalize the electric body. They are rich in plant-based iron, which supports the brain, lymphatic system and central nervous system. They also support proper kidney and respiratory function, as well as help to reduce cravings for addictive substances.

Diuretic:
Fucus vesiculosus - This herb acts as a natural diuretic. It helps flush excessive stagnant fluid from the body; supports the removal dead cells and helps promote healthy skin. It is high in plant-based magnesium, calcium, phosphate and many other minerals.

Male Hormonal Support:
Sarsaparilla, yohimbe, sensitiva, chaparo amargo - These herbs support, balance and nourish the male endocrine system. They support improved sexual responsiveness, increased virility, and improved blood flow to the male genitalia.

Female Hormonal Support:
Damiana, hortensia, sarsaparilla, Irish sea moss - These herbs have been noted to support, balance and nourish the female endocrine reproductive system. They support improved fertility and overall sexual appetite that may be decreased because of an unhealthy reproductive system.

Blood Nourishment:

Chapparal, burdock, yellowdock, nopal, ortiga and sarsaparilla - These herbs can play an important role in nourishing and cleansing the blood. They are high in iron phosphate and many other minerals. They have been shown to nourish and strengthen the entire system of the electric body.

Twenty

TAKING CHARGE

"I didn't know him that well. I mean, I knew him. I knew him, and I happened to be planning to be in Florida and I thought it would be fun to go to his wedding because it's always entertaining. Now that he's running for president, it's a little more troubling."

— **HILLARY CLINTON**, EXPLAINING HOW SHE CAME TO BE IN A FRONT ROW SEAT FOR DONALD TRUMP'S 2005 WEDDING

"The thought of what America would be like If the Classics had a wide circulation Troubles my sleep, The thought of what America, The thought of what America, The thought of what America would be like If the Classics had a wide circulation Troubles my sleep. Nunc dimittis, now lettest thou thy servant, Now lettest thou thy servant Depart in peace. The thought of what America, The thought of what America, The thought of what America would be like If the Classics had a wide circulation... Oh well! It troubles my sleep.

— **EZRA POUND**, "CANTICO DEL SOLE," IN PERSONAE (1926)

C hoosing a doctor or any other life partner is a bit like choosing a pig in a poke at the Iowa State Fair: at the first meeting, neither party knows whether the relationship in the long run will be more like when Harry met Sally or more like when Charlie Manson met Lynette ("Squeaky") Fromme. The same goes for choosing a President or for choosing a prophylactic brand. In the end, we have to make a choice, even if the only choices we have are the bearded lady or the tiger.

We live in the best possible of all possible worlds, but for the over-whelming majority of people on this planet, life is no bowl of cherries. That said, things could always be worse, even for the guy with an Isis sword about to chop off his head. While we are alive, it is incumbent on us to live life to the fullest and to contribute to the health, happiness and well-being of our families, friends, neighbors, and even to total strangers, via Federal benefits programs and the annual collection for missionary work at the local Catholic Church.

For most of us, it is enough to cultivate our own gardens; others strive to heal the sick and rule the universe through activities of the highest level such as running repeatedly for high office; running a brain surgery clinic in Washington, D.C.; building skating rinks, walls, skyscrapers, gambling dens and golf courses emblazoned with your family name; running great companies to the ground for fun and profit; hosting a nightly news/en-tertainment program on Fox News Channel; defending the record of a brother who sold us down the river; reading the works of Doctor Seuss on the Senate floor; helping your father sell gold by proclaiming and has-tening a national financial crisis; conducting traffic studies in New Jersey; surrendering your microphone to African-American empowerment activ-ists; auditioning for the zombie apocalypse; and writing books to expose the nefarious activities of the Control System, which buys and pays for the stage where all these power plays unravel and spin again.

Young Hillary Rodham probably didn't have a chance to meet too many Gretchens or Penelopes at the Scranton lace mill or at her daddy's textile supply business; but by the time the country is ready to make its choice, Hillary, like Donald Trump, will have met and interacted with thousands of incredibly smart and beautiful women with polysyllabic, exotic names. Her girl Friday, Huma Abedin Wiener (aka Carlos Danger), has been compared and contrasted favorably with Amal Alamuddin Clooney (a member of Julian Assange's legal dream team). In case you were wondering, Huma's husband has been banned from interacting with the candidate, but his employer, MWW Group, Inc., was founded and is currently headed by Michael Kempner, one of Hillary's top bundlers, who was the National Finance Co-Chairman of Hillary for President in 2008.

During Bill Clinton's first term in office, Hillary Clinton was derided for failing at her social duties as First Lady because she preferred to spend her days and evenings attending health care policy meetings. She has since come into her own as a social butterfly. Hillary has danced with Ellen DeGeneres; supped with potentates and harem members of Middle Eastern royal families; and even attended Donald Trump's wedding to Slovenian-American top (sometimes nude) model Melania Knauss.

Unlike Hillary's Benghazi nightmare, the Trump wedding was one of the more successful ventures Mrs. Clinton participated in commemorating. Like Marla Maples before her, Melania is one satisfied customer: "We have incredible sex at least once a day, sometimes even more," she told radio star Howard Stern in 2000.

White House dinners under a Trump administration promise to be among the most star-studded events in history, with Kanye West, Jay-Z and Beyoncé certain to be among the headline entertainers featured at the President's eye-popping, shoulder-rubbing shindigs and soirées.

Presidential hospitality was not always so glamorous. FDR famously brought his neighbors from Poughkeepsie breadlines, soup kitchens and ladies' auxiliary groups to eat hotdogs with the King of England.

A White House State Dinner or tea party suddenly became the biggest ticket in the country when Jackie and Jack Kennedy began to include names such as Earl Wild, Pablo Casals, Igor Stravinsky and Grace Bumbry as part of the after-dinner or post-prandial entertainment. Kennedy, of course, is best remembered for his birthday celebrations with Marilyn Monroe and Frank Sinatra.

When Lyndon Johnson's people took over the event planning, outdoor grilling was once again the culinary attraction. Those who threw their tickets in the toilet lived to regret it once they learned that Tchaikovsky Competition winner Van Cliburn, a son of Texas, performed for the starstruck outdoor barbecue guests at LBJ's ranch.

Nixon and Ford had little use for entertainment as they fought off the demons of Vietnam, Watergate and inflation, but both made sure that Bob Hope and Billy Graham were invited to any gathering of a convivial nature. When Nixon did entertain, he was mostly partial to jazz. Luckily, according to journalist Wil Haygood (the man behind the 2013 film *The Butler*) in a January 2013 feature story on Presidential entertaining for *Town and Country Magazine,* Counsellor to the President Leonard Garment knew all the jazz stars worth knowing. Marian McPartland, Duke Ellington and Sammy Davis, Jr. were among Nixon's hapless serenaders. Ellington, who was invited to the White House on the occasion of his 70th birthday, invited his friend Clifford Alexander, Jr., whom Nixon had fired as EEOC Director, only to be told that he had to rescind the invitation because Alexander was prominently featured on Nixon's famous Enemies List.

Jimmy Carter, who knew his classical music and played a steady stream of Rubinstein and Horowitz records in the Oval Office, went straight to the top and got Vladimir Horowitz to perform for a group of bureaucrats and Georgian dowagers who probably would have preferred to hear Conway Twitty or Glen Campbell.

For the most part, Carter's events were not all that lively because Carter banned hard alcohol at White House events. It was probably a wise move, because the biggest scandal during the Carter years was Hamilton Jordan's drunken comment to Jehan Sadat at a state dinner for the President of Egypt. Jordan, who was reputed to be a big fan of unsafe sex with strangers and cocaine, allegedly took the occasion of Mrs. Sadat's momentary wardrobe malfunction to exclaim, "I've always wanted to see the pyramids!"

Ronald Reagan asked Horowitz for an encore White House performance in 1986. That occasion was memorable not only for Horowitz' playing of Schumann and Moszkowski, but also because Nancy Reagan slipped and fell off the platform during her husband's remarks after the performance. Reagan was ready with one of his inimitable ad-libs: "Honey, I told you to do that only if they didn't applaud."

State dinners were not quite as glorious during the Clinton years. President Clinton and his wife were unable to summon Horowitz back from the dead, so they made do with lesser lights such as Sharon Stone and Barbara Streisand, who had to time-share the coveted spot in the Lincoln Bedroom with a multitude of Democratic campaign donors and wealthy lobbyists, and with the occasional Brzezinski pal or Trilateral Commission member fallen on hard times. Sidney Blumenthal, who is currently working on a definitive three-volume history of Lincoln's political life, was only able to look at the famous long bed with longing. Tragically, the only days available for such a sojourn were Passover, Chanukah and Sukkot, days when the super-observant Blumenthal was not really supposed to travel, turn on an electric switch or even use a cellphone.

The less said about George Bush and his addiction to songs like "God Bless the U.S.A" and "Achy, Breaky Heart," the better.

Yes, Presidents and their billionaire backers and flunkies and fluffers and interns and jesters and basketball buddies and spiritual advisors and legal advisors have a glorious time hanging out separately and together, but life in the White House is not all fun and games.

The most important person in a President's life is often the person who gives him the daily morphine, Botox or Oxycodone or steroid injections before the daily CIA briefings and before bedtime. With the possible exception of Barack Obama, Bill Clinton and the four stone heads on Mount Rushmore, most of the people who made it to the point of making an Inaugural Address on the Capitol steps were so old and so sick that premature ejaculations and acne were often no longer a concern.

Americans have had to get used to Presidents dying in office or otherwise fumbling the nuclear football. William Henry Harrison lasted about a month before giving up the ghost. Several Presidents who enjoyed reasonable health ended up being shot to death.

Woodrow Wilson was so incapacitated by a stroke that his young wife had to run the government. Edith Bolling Galt Wilson would be on all the Presidential class posters in America were it not for the fact that her husband's illness, like Vladimir Lenin's final illness, had to be kept a closely-guarded secret to prevent the assumption of the Presidency by Vice

President Thomas Marshall, who did not want to deal with the headaches associated with running the country.

Franklin Roosevelt, whose physical disabilities caused by polio were relegated to the realm of plausible deniability by the collusion of news cameramen who usually refrained from shooting newsreel footage when his wheelchair was in use, is remembered today as a man of astonishing vigor and playfulness. He is also remembered for the his gaunt, haggard appearance at the Yalta talks where he all but gave away the store to Stalin. In twelve years at the helm as Commander in Chief, the President had visibly aged more than most dogs in the same number of years.

JFK, for all his appearance of robust health, lived in excruciating pain for most of his tenure in the White House. Some scholars of his Presidency claim that he would not likely have survived a second term if he had somehow dodged Oswald's single bullet.

Richard Nixon was a deeply paranoid and secretive individual. He was a creep's creep if ever there was such a thing. *The Final Days*, Woodward and Bernstein's blow-by-blow account of the last 17 days of Nixon's time in office, presents the image of an emotional cripple desperately trying to come to terms with the biggest disgrace in American history.

Ronald Reagan would be remembered today as just another victim of Washington, D.C.'s senseless gun violence if the "Devastator" bullets in John Hinckley's revolver had exploded as advertised and as intended. Instead, he lived to forget everything and everyone he ever knew. There are those who dispute that Reagan's memory began its steady decline during his two terms of office, but many of us wondered how he could forget such very memorable deeds as trading arms for Iranian-held hostages. Reagan's biographer Edmund Morris was granted a number of sittings for a word portrait that turned out to be more faithful to Reagan's dreams than to any coherent vision of reality.

One of the problems of writing about Reagan is that he apparently conflated his own experiences with movie scripts and TV commercials he had performed. In his own mind, real life be damned, Reagan was by turns a football star, a Navy hellcat and a chimpanzee baby sitter. Morris realized that the only honorable way to respond to the challenge of dealing with such an unreliable witness of his own life was to add the spice of fiction.

What will become of Donald Trump during his four years at the pinnacle of power and influence? Will Trump's famous mane still be largely intact? Now that he has made it to the White House, the true answers to these questions will probably never become known to the public. I bet Trump will continue to deny he colors his hair?

There were many issues debated in the 2016 campaign. Education is one of the most important: people want to know whether the best model for molding our nation's youth is the Common Core curriculum, the Trump University scam model, the Harvard/Yale path blazed by Ted Cruz and Hillary Clinton, or the Sunday school approach that has worked so effectively for Ben Carson.

Another big issue was General Motors and the car industry writ large. Was Obama right to save a company famous for making cars that are "unsafe at any speed"? Should Ford be forced to make all its cars in Detroit again? Does Donald Trump know how to drive? Should the lying, cheating folks at Volkswagen be allowed to sell their cars to decent-churchgoing Americans?

Illegal immigration would probably not have come up if Donald Trump had not proclaimed Mexico a nation of rapists and promised to build a beautiful wall to keep them out. Now that he has been elected the 45th President, it will be very interesting to see if he really builds the wall. Be that as it may, there are many serious problems with the idea of trying to maintain a society where an increasingly large underclass lives in the shadows like in the Pretoria of the 1970s or Tel Aviv since 1948.

Before the 2008 election, the U.S. government was near total financial collapse in the wake of Lehman Brothers declaration of bankruptcy. By the time of Obama's scheduled departure from office, we can probably expect to have lived through eight years of relative peace and prosperity. Nevertheless, financial chaos can occur at any time in this age of terrorism, financial speculation and Republican intransigence on matters ranging from climate change and deficit spending to reviving the gold standard and cutting taxes to zero or less for people who donate a threshold amount for purposes of holding the Republican National Convention. Democrats, although they hold very little national power outside the White House, also have the ability to unhinge the economy by promoting social unrest, labor activism, minimum wage increases, job-killing regulations, limitations on fracking and oil profiteering, failure to construct the Keystone pipeline, and the unwitting instigation of a socialist or Communist revolution.

Given the daunting challenges just listed, and the paucity of qualified people to manage these problems, even those not involved as puppet masters of the Control System could be forgiven for not wanting to rock the boat by making sure that the nuclear codes are turned over to Donald Trump, who certainly seems at this point to be the lesser of about 20 evils. However, given everything we have learned in the course of going through this book, even lifetime members of the Council on Foreign Relations have the right to ask, "What will become of us? How will we survive the next decade intact as a nation? How can we groom another Ronald Reagan in time to save us from the horrors that await us with a chicken hawk ready to launch full-scale military attacks on misogynistic societies that few people outside the Beltway and the CFR meeting rooms have even heard of?"

No one knows what challenges and opportunities the future will bring, nor do we know whether Trump Unleashed might not surpass the worst fantasies of Ed Klein and Trey Gowdy. Will Puerto Rico and Washington, D.C. finally become the 51st and 52nd states? Will Trump launch Trident missiles against Iran, Russia, Saudi Arabia or some other country not yet on the map or in the news? Will some other Blumenthal emerge to save the world from famine, Depression or nuclear war? Will Trump make public the FBI files, the secret Monica Lewinsky recordings and the sordid e-mail correspondence of Bill Clinton? Will television stations be required to broadcast equal hours of programming in Spanish and English? Will Obama and Eric Holder replace Thomas and Scalia on the Supreme Court? Will guns be relegated to the dustbin of history? With IBM's Watson firmly in charge of weather information distribution, will we finally be able to figure out how to forestall planetary extinction by changing our planet's climate for the better? That's a lot for anyone's plate!

As it appears from the vantage point of November 2015, these are the kind of things that will keep Donald Trump and all other Americans awake at night. While he and they are asleep during broad daylight, the monopolists who control the financial system will take ever-bolder steps to integrate the American healthcare system into their portfolio of doom.

The electoral success of Donald Trump may not doom our prospects as a nation; indeed, any of the other alternatives currently on offer seem about as enticing as a cold shower in a Zyklon B-equipped van. Regardless of the fact that we are likely to survive his four or eight years more or less intact, we should all take the opportunity to investigate whether there is any better way to maintain our health and improve our mental outlook than surrendering all control over our healthcare decisions to electronic brains in the cloud; Harvard-educated doctors who think that the healing process is all about chemical and electronic brain stimulation; health insurance professionals who see the prolongation of a young life on life support systems as an opportunity for Medicare waste, fraud and abuse; and drug companies run by hedge fund managers who seek to maximize their profits by bilking sick people for the cost of the substances that are helping to hasten their demise.

I think the most important piece of advice I can offer in these coming hard times is that you should never surrender to fear. Donald Trump and his handlers will offer prescriptions based on their best guess of what might work, but they don't have all the answers. If you have taken anything away from the twists and turns in this book, it should be that nothing is what it appears to be, and no business or political leader in this nation is or will ever be fully transparent about his motivations and purposes. There is no advantage to be gained in succumbing to the altar of the white coat and stethoscope, or to mindless hero-worship inspired by the Presidential Seal and the domination of the news and gossip pages by those close to the centers of financial and political power. Presidents put their pants on one leg at a time. Doctors are as likely to be Moonies or Scientologists or Seventh Day Adventists as the rest of us. Knowledge of the intricacies of the periodic table or the minutiae of Constitutional law does not necessarily guarantee a person a long and happy life. A doctor or politician has the same faculties of hearing and seeing and carving turkey meat on Thanksgiving as any other citizen.

The progress of medical science has been a joy to see in many respects, but the disappointments and false promises often overwhelm what should be a great source of pride for our nation. It turns out that doctors don't live much longer on average than the rest of us. Most men check out in their seventies and women tend to make it to 80 or above. Having a medical degree from Johns Hopkins may end up getting you an extra two or three months of life, but most of your fellow citizens are roughly keeping pace, whether they are your patients or not.

Americans have to learn to think for themselves and stand up for themselves. We have let one industry after another surrender to the people with the biggest money bags, but our health is too important to allow its maintenance and enhancement to be completely subsumed to the needs of predatory insurance companies and greedy drug companies and faceless government bureaucrats. It is a great thing if the primary consequence of Obamacare is that fewer people die in the streets of easily preventable or treatable conditions; but it would be an equally terrible tragedy if we let the existence of a monopoly-controlled top-down healthcare system determine how we live our lives down to the smallest detail. Human beings need more than medication schedules and yearly checkups with nurse practitioners to be able to say at the end of their lives, "I am proud that I was born an American."

I fully realize that the kind of strict diet I have proposed in this book would be a tough sell to most Americans, since it is much easier to buy bags full of processed foods and frozen vegetables and potato chips and soda and ice cream. You may eat this way every day and still live to the ripe old age of 75 or 80, as most people do. From the bottom of my heart, I hope you will have the courage to take a different path.

I may live no longer than you, but I make it a point to learn something every day about how to fill my stomach lining and brain cells with elements that give me energy and help me reach and expand the outer limits of my mental and physical capacities. It's not just about adding years to your life; you also need to think about how to add life to your years.

It is easy to give in to the idea all human efforts are in vain because one day we will die. Banish all such thoughts from your mind! Get up tomorrow and live like you have something to prove. Start with a set of push-ups; have a non-GMO organic apple; and then get to work diligently and intelligently in order to bring about a better world for yourself and your significant others, which should include all members of the human species. Don't let Donald Trump hold up the world on his shoulders while you live the sheltered existence of a pack rat in a crowded New Jersey apartment. Be a gym rat, not a lab rat. Participate actively in your community. Find out who the cheaters and scammers are, and call them to account. When you receive a medical bill or insurance company statement, don't assume it's even close to accurate. Learn to argue and win against the forces that are trying to control you. Strive for independence, self-control and moderation in all things except healthy eating habits and vigorous daily physical exercise. Teach your children well. Keep them away from drug pushers and pill pushers of all persuasions to the best of your ability, so help you God!

I know of no better way to end this book than to give a little pull on my ears like Carol Burnett used to do, and say goodbye until we meet again. I'm so glad we had this time together. Live long and prosper! Be healthy and be well! *Valē!*

Twenty-One

1969: DR. DAY'S PREDICTIONS AND THE NEW WORLD ORDER (PART 1)

THE SECRET MARCH 20, 1969 LECTURE:
Dr. Lawrence Dunegan, MD Recalling the Talk Dr. Richard Day, MD Gave

"World events do not occur by accident. They are made to happen,
whether it is to do with national issues or commerce; and most of
them are staged and managed by those who hold the purse strings."

— DENNIS HEALY, UK SECRETARY OF STATE FOR
DEFENSE FROM 1964 TO 1970 AND CHANCELLOR
OF THE EXCHEQUER FROM 1974 TO 1979.

D r. Richard Day, M.D. taught at Mount Sinai from 1968 until he re-
tired in 1971. Earlier in his career, he was the National Medical
Director of Planned Parenthood (1965-1968); Professor and Chairman
of the Department of Pediatrics at the University of Pittsburgh (1956
to 1965); Professor and Chairman of the Department of Pediatrics in

the Downstate Medical School in Brooklyn (1953 to 1956) and Associate Professor at the College of Physicians and Surgeons, Columbia University (1935 to 1953).

Dr. Lawrence Dunegan, M.D. was invited to attend a lecture given by Dr. Richard Day M.D. on March 20, 1969 to 80-90 Medical Doctors. Dr. Richard Day was an insider admitting that indeed there was an organized power group of men, who wielded enough influence to determine major events involving countries around the world, and he expounded on changes that were planned for the remainder of the 20th century.

The Following transcript is part one from the U.S. Coalition for Life. The following is a transcript of the first of three tapes on the "New Order of Barbarians", referred to on the tapes simply as the "New World System." Tapes one and two, done in 1988, are the reminiscences By Dr. Lawrence Dunegan M.D., of a speech given March 20, 1969 by Dr. Richard Day.

It's interesting to note that Dr. Dunegan *"spilled the beans"* in 1988. According to the bio information, Dr. Day died shortly thereafter, in 1989. It could be a coincidence since Dr. Day was elderly when he died, and then again....

Most of you reading this are very well aware, already, of many of the details involved in the diabolical plan to bring about a New World Order. As much as we all know, hearing about the "HOW" from the words of an insider is spine chilling. I believe these tapes could change many lives and awaken many more people to the reality of what lies ahead if we don't stop the process. There are many more millions of us than there are of the planners. The useful idiots –

their words, not ours — who are helping the process along know not what they do. If they did know, they would stop, because they would know that they, too, will be either terminated or become part of a Global Slave Camp.

Dr. Dunegan reveals not just "WHAT" is intended for America and all people in the world, but "HOW" the controllers intend to carry out their plan. He covers topics such as:

- IS there a power, a force or a group of men organizing and redirecting change?
- "Everything is in place and nobody can stop us now . . ."
- People will have to get used to change — everything will change, constantly
- The REAL and the "STATED" goals
- Population Control
- Permission to have babies
- Redirecting the purpose of sex - sex without reproduction and reproduction without sex
- Sex education as a tool of World Government
- Encouraging homosexuality... Sex, anything goes
- Euthanasia and the "Demise Pill"
- Limiting access to affordable medical care makes eliminating the elderly easier
- Planning the control over medicine
- Elimination of private doctors
- New Difficult to diagnose and untreatable diseases
- Suppressing cancer cures as a means of population control.
- Inducing heart attacks as a form of assassination
- Education as a tool for accelerating the onset of puberty and pushing evolution and MUCH, MUCH MORE

IS THERE A POWER, A FORCE OR A GROUP OF MEN ORGANIZING AND REDIRECTING CHANGE?

There has been much written, and much said, by some people who have looked at all the changes that have occurred in American society in the past 20 years or so, and who have looked retrospectively to earlier history of the United States, and indeed, of the world, and come to the conclusion that there is a conspiracy of sorts which influences, indeed controls, major historical events, not only in the United States, but around the world. This conspiratorial interpretation of history is based on people making observations from the outside, gathering evidence and coming to the conclusion that from the outside they see a conspiracy. Their evidence and conclusions are based on evidence gathered in retrospect. Period.

I want to now describe what I heard from a speaker in 1969 which in several weeks will be 20 years ago. The speaker did not speak in terms of retrospect, but rather predicting changes that would be brought about in the future. The speaker was not looking from the outside in, thinking that he saw conspiracy, rather, he was on the inside, admitting that, indeed, there was an organized power, force, group of men, who wielded enough influence to determine major events involving countries around the world. And he predicted, or rather expounded on, changes that were planned for the remainder of this century.

As you listen, if you can recall the situation, at least in the United States in 1969 and the few years thereafter, and then recall the kinds of changes which have occurred between then and now, almost 20 years later, I believe you will be impressed with the degree to which the things that were planned to be brought about have already been accomplished. Some of the things that were discussed were not intended to be accomplished yet by 1988. [Ed. Note: the year Dr. Dunegan made this tape] but are intended to be accomplished before the end of this century. There is a timetable; and it was during this session that some of the elements of the timetable were brought out.

Anyone who recalls early in the days of the Kennedy Presidency...the Kennedy campaign...when he spoke of "progress in the decade of the '60s"; that was kind of a cliché in those days - "the decade of the '60s." Well, by 1969 our speaker was talking about the decade of the '70s, the decade of the '80s, and the decade of the '90s. So that...

I think that terminology that we are looking at. . . looking at things and expressing things, probably all comes from the same source. Prior to that time I don't remember anybody saying "the decade of the '40s and the decade of the '50s.

So I think this overall plan and timetable had taken important shape with more predictability to those who control it, sometime in the late '50s. That's speculation on my part. In any event, the speaker said that his purpose was to tell us about changes which would be brought about in the next 30 years or so . . . so that an entirely new world-wide system would be in operation before the turn of the century. As he put it, "We plan to enter the 21st Century with a running start. **Everything is in place and nobody can stop us now . . ."**

He said – as we listened to what he was about to present – he said, *"Some of you will think I'm talking about Communism. Well, what I'm talking about is much bigger than Communism!"*

At that time he indicated that there is much more cooperation between East and West than most people realize. In his introductory remarks he commented that he was free to speak at this time because now, and I'm quoting here, "everything is in place and nobody can stop us now." That's the end of that quotation. He went on to say that most people don't understand how governments operate and even people in high positions in governments, including our own, don't really understand how and where decisions are made.

He went on to say that... he went on to say that people who really influence decisions are names that, for the most part, would be familiar to most of us, but he would not use individuals' names or names of any specific organization. But, that if he did, most of the people would be names that were recognized by most of his audience. He went on to say that they were not primarily people in public office, but people of prominence who were primarily known in their private occupations or private positions.

The speaker was a doctor of medicine, a former professor at a large Eastern university, and he was addressing a group of doctors of medicine, about 80 in number. His name would not be widely recognized by anybody likely to hear this, and so there is no point in giving his name. The only purpose in recording this is that it may give a perspective to those who hear it regarding the changes which have already been accomplished in the past 20 years or so, and a bit of a preview to what at least some people are planning for the remainder of this century so that we – or they – would enter the 21st Century with a flying start. Some of us may not enter that Century.

His purpose in telling our group about these changes that were to be brought about was to make it easier for us to adapt to these changes. Indeed, as he quite accurately said, they would be and he hopes that we, as sort of his friends, would make the adaptation more easily if we knew somewhat beforehand what to expect.

"PEOPLE WILL HAVE TO GET USED TO CHANGE . . ."

Somewhere in the introductory remarks he insisted that nobody have a tape recorder and that nobody take notes, which for a professor was a very remarkable kind of thing to expect from an audience. Something in his remarks suggested that there could be negative repercussions against him if his... if it became widely known what he was about to say to... our group... if it became widely known that he spilled the beans, so to speak.

When I heard that, first I thought maybe that was sort of an ego trip, somebody enhancing his own importance. But as the revelations unfolded, I began to understand why he might have had some concern about not having it widely known what was said, although this... although this was a fairly public forum where he was speaking, [where the] remarks were delivered. But, nonetheless, he asked that no notes be taken... no tape recording be used – suggesting there might be some personal danger to himself if these revelations were widely publicized.

Again, as the remarks began to unfold, and I saw the rather outrageous things that were said – at that time they certainly seemed outrageous -- I made it a point to try to remember as much of what he said as I could, and during the subsequent weeks and months and years, to connect my recollections to simple events around me, both to aid my memory for the future in case I wanted to do what I'm doing now - record this. And also, to try to maintain a perspective on what would be developing, if indeed, it followed the predicted pattern - which it has!

At this point, so that I don't forget to include it later, I'll just include some statements that were made from time to time throughout the presentation... just having a general bearing on the whole presentation. One of the statements had to do with change. People get used. . the statement was, *"People will have to get used to the idea of change, so used to change, that they'll be expecting change. Nothing will be permanent."*

This often came out in the context of a society of... where people seemed to have no roots or moorings, but would be passively willing to accept change simply because it was all they had ever known. This was sort of in contrast to generations of people up until this time where certain things you expected to be, and remain in place as reference points for your life. So change was to be brought about, change was to be anticipated and expected, and accepted, no questions asked. Another comment that was made from time to time during the presentation was, *"People are too trusting. People don't ask the right questions."*

Sometimes, being too trusting was equated with being too dumb. But sometimes when... when he would say that and say, *"People don't ask the right questions,"* it was almost with a sense of regret, as if he were uneasy with what he was part of, and wished that people would challenge it and maybe not be so trusting.

THE REAL AND THE "STATED" GOALS

Another comment that was repeated from time to time... this particularly in relation to changing laws and customs... and specific changes... he said, *"Everything has two purposes. One is the ostensible purpose which will make it acceptable to people; and second, is the real purpose which would further the goals of establishing the new system and having it."*

Frequently he would say, *"There is just no other way. There's just no other way!"*

This seemed to come as a sort of an apology, particularly when... at the conclusion of describing some particularly offensive changes; for example, the promotion of drug addiction which we'll get into shortly.

POPULATION CONTROL

He was very active with population control groups, the population control movement, and population control was really the entry point into specifics following the introduction. He said the population is growing too fast. Numbers of people living at any one time on the planet must be limited or we will run out of space to live. We will outgrow our food supply and we will over-pollute the world with our waste.

PERMISSION TO HAVE BABIES

People won't be allowed to have babies just because they want to or because they are careless. Most families would be limited to two. Some people would be allowed only one, and the outstanding person or persons might be selected and allowed to have three. But most people would [be] allowed to have only two babies. That's because the zero population growth [rate] is 2.1 children per completed family. So something like every 10th family might be allowed the privilege of the third baby.

To me, up to this point, the word *"population control"* primarily connoted limiting the number of babies to be born. But this remark, about what people would be *"allowed"* and then what followed, made it quite clear that when you hear "population control" that means more than just controlling births. It means control of every endeavor of an entire... of the entire world population; a much broader meaning to that term than I had ever attached to it before hearing this. As you listen and reflect back on some of the things you hear, you will begin to recognize how one aspect dovetails with other aspects in terms of controlling human endeavors.

REDIRECTING THE PURPOSE OF SEX - SEX WITHOUT REPRODUCTION AND REPRODUCTION WITHOUT SEX

Well, from population control, the natural next step then was sex. He said sex must be separated from reproduction. Sex is too pleasurable, and the urges are too strong, to expect people to give it up. Chemicals in food and in the water supply to reduce the sex drive is not practical. The strategy then would be not to diminish sex activity, but to increase sex activity, but in such a way that people won't be having babies.

CONTRACEPTION UNIVERSALLY AVAILABLE TO ALL

And the first consideration then here was contraception. Contraception would be very strongly encouraged, and it would be connected so closely in people's minds with sex, that they would automatically think contraception when they were thinking or preparing for sex. And contraception would be made universally available. Nobody wanting contraception would be... find that they were unavailable.

Contraceptives would be displayed much more prominently in drug stores, right up with the cigarettes and chewing gum. Out in the open, rather than hidden under the counter where people would have to ask for them and maybe be embarrassed. This kind of openness was a way of suggesting that contraceptions . . that contraceptives are just as much a part of life as any other items sold in the store. And, contraceptives would be advertised. And, contraceptives would be dispensed in the schools in association with sex education!

SEX EDUCATION AS A TOOL OF WORLD GOVERNMENT

The sex education was to get kids interested early, making the connection between sex and the need for contraception early in their lives, even before they became very active. At this point I was recalling some of my teachers, particularly in high school and found it totally unbelievable to think of them agreeing, much less participating in, distributing of contraceptives to students. But, that only reflected my lack of understanding of how these people operate. That was before the school-based clinic programs got started.

Many, many cities in the United States by this time have already set up school-based clinics which are primarily contraception, birth control, population control clinics. The idea then is that the connection between sex and contraception introduced and reinforced in school would carry over into marriage. Indeed, if young people – when they matured – decided to get married, marriage itself would be diminished in importance. He indicated some recognition that most people probably would want to be married... but that this certainly would not be any longer considered to be necessary for sexual activity.

TAX FUNDED ABORTION AS POPULATION CONTROL

No surprise then, that the next item was abortion. And this, now back in 1969, four years before Roe vs. Wade. He said, *"Abortion will no longer be a crime. Abortion will be accepted as normal"*, and would be paid for by taxes for people who could not pay for their own abortions. Contraceptives would be made available by tax money so that nobody would have to do without contraceptives. If school sex programs would lead to more pregnancies in children, that was really seen as no problem. Parents who think they are opposed to abortion on moral or religious grounds will change their minds when it is their own child who is pregnant. So this will help overcome opposition to abortion. Before long, only a few die-hards will still refuse to see abortion as acceptable, and they won't matter anymore.

ENCOURAGING HOMOSEXUALITY. SEX, ANYTHING GOES

Homosexuality also was to be encouraged. *"People will be given permission to be homosexual."*

That's the way it was stated. They won't have to hide it. And elderly people will be encouraged to continue to have active sex lives into the very old ages, just as long as they can. Everyone will be given permission to have sex, to enjoy however they want. Anything goes. This is the way it was put. And, I remember thinking, *"how arrogant for this individual, or whoever he represents, to feel that they can give or withhold permission for people to do things!"* But that was the terminology that was used.

In this regard, clothing was mentioned. Clothing styles would be made more stimulating and provocative. Recall back in 1969 was the time of the mini skirt, when those mini- skirts were very, very high and revealing. He said, *"It is not just the amount of skin that is exposed that makes clothing sexually seductive, but other, more subtle things are often suggestive,"*

...things like movement, and the cut of clothing, and the kind of fabric, the positioning of accessories on the clothing. *"If a woman has an attractive body, why should she not show it?"* was one of the statements.

There was not detail on what was meant by *"provocative clothing,"* but since that time if you watched the change in clothing styles, blue jeans are cut in a way that they're more tight-fitting in the crotch. They form wrinkles. Wrinkles are essentially arrows. Lines which direct one's vision to certain anatomic areas. And, this was around the time of the "burn your bra" activity. He indicated that a lot of women should not go without a bra. They need a bra to be attractive, so instead of banning bras and burning them, bras would come back. But they would be thinner and softer allowing more natural movement. It was not specifically stated, but certainly a very thin bra is much more revealing of the nipple and what else is underneath, than the heavier bras that were in style up to that time.

Technology. Earlier he said...sex and reproduction would be separated. You would have sex without reproduction and then technology was reproduction without sex. This would be done in the laboratory. He indicated that already, much, much research was underway about making babies in the laboratory. There was some elaboration on that, but I don't remember the details, how much of that technology has come to my attention since that time. I don't remember . . I don't remember in a way that I can distinguish what was said from what I subsequently have learned as general medical information.

FAMILIES TO DIMINISH IN IMPORTANCE

Families would be limited in size. We already alluded to not being allowed more than two children. Divorce would be made easier and more prevalent. Most people who marry will marry more than once. More people will not marry. Unmarried people would stay in hotels and even live together. That would be very common - nobody would even ask questions about it. It would be widely accepted as no different from married people being together.

More women will work outside the home. More men will be transferred to other cities, and in their jobs, more men would travel. Therefore, it would be harder for families to stay together. This would tend to make the marriage relationship less stable and, therefore, tend to make people less willing to have babies. And, the extended families would be smaller, and more remote. Travel would be easier, less expensive, <u>for a while</u>, so that people who did have to travel would feel they could get back to their families... not that they were abruptly being made remote from their families.

But one of the net effects of easier divorce laws combined with the promotion of travel, and transferring families from one city to another, was to create instability in the families. If both husband and wife are working and one partner gets transferred the other one may not be easily transferred. So one either keeps his or her job and stays behind while the other leaves, or else gives up the job and risks not finding employment in the new location. Rather a diabolical approach to this whole thing.

EUTHANASIA AND THE "DEMISE PILL"

Everybody has a right to live only so long. The old are no longer useful. They become a burden. You should be ready to accept death. Most people are. An arbitrary age limit could be established. After all, you have a right to only so many steak dinners, so many orgasms, and so many good pleasures in life. And after you have had enough of them and you're no longer productive, working, and contributing, then you should be ready to step aside for the next generation.

Some things that would help people realize that they had lived long enough, he mentioned several of these... I don't remember them all... here are a few: Use of very pale printing ink on forms that people... are necessary... to fill out, so that older people wouldn't be able to read the pale ink as easily and would need to go to younger people for help. Automobile traffic patterns - there would be more high-speed traffic lanes .. traffic patterns that would .. that older people with their slower reflexes would have trouble dealing with and thus, lose some of their independence.

LIMITING ACCESS TO AFFORDABLE MEDICAL CARE MAKES ELIMINATING THE ELDERLY EASIER

A big item – [that] was elaborated at some length – was the cost of medical care would be burdensomely high. Medical care would be connected very closely with one's work, but also would be made very, very high in cost so that it would simply be unavailable to people beyond a certain time. And unless they had a remarkably rich, supporting family, they would just have to do without care.

And the idea was that if everybody says, *"Enough! What a burden it is on the young to try to maintain the old people,"* then the young would become agreeable to helping Mom and Dad along the way, provided this was done humanely and with dignity. And then the real example was - there could be like a nice, farewell party, a real celebration. Mom and Dad had done a good job. And then after the party's over they take the *"demise pill."*

PLANNING THE CONTROL OVER MEDICINE

The next topic is Medicine. There would be profound changes in the practice of medicine. Overall, medicine would be much more tightly controlled. The observation was made, *"Congress is not going to go along with national health insurance. That (in 1969), he said, "is now, abundantly evident. But it's not necessary. We have other ways to control health care."*

These would come about more gradually, but all health care delivery would come under tight control. Medical care would be closely connected to work. If you don't work or can't work, you won't have access to medical care. The days of hospitals giving away free care would gradually wind down, to where it was virtually non-existent. Costs would be forced up so that people won't be able to afford to go without insurance. People pay... you pay for it, you're entitled to it.

It was only subsequently that I began to realize the extent to which you would not be paying for it. Your medical care would be paid for by others. And therefore you would gratefully accept, on bended knee, what was offered to you as a privilege. Your role being responsible for your own care would be diminished.

As an aside here – this is not something that was developed at this time... I didn't understand it at the time — as an aside, the way this works, everybody's made dependent on insurance. And if you don't have insurance then you pay directly; the cost of your care is enormous. The insurance company, however, paying for your care, does not pay that same amount. If you are charged, say, $600 on your part, they pay $300 or $400. And that differential in billing has the desired effect: It enables the insurance company to pay for that which you could never pay for. They get a discount that's unavailable to you. When you see your bill you're grateful that the insurance company could do that. And in this way you are dependent, and virtually required to have insurance. The whole billing is fraudulent.

Anyhow, continuing on now... access to hospitals would be tightly controlled. Identification would be needed to get into the building. The security in and around hospitals would be established and gradually increased so that nobody without identification could get in or move around inside the building. Theft of hospital equipment, things like typewriters and microscopes and so forth would be *"allowed"* and exaggerated; reports of it would be exaggerated so that this would be the excuse needed to establish the need for strict security, until people got used to it. And anybody moving about in a hospital would be required to wear an identification badge with photograph and . . telling why he was there . . employee or lab technician or visitor or whatever.

This is to be brought in gradually — getting everybody used to the idea of identifying themselves — until it was just accepted. This need for ID to move about would start in small ways: hospitals, some businesses, but gradually expand to include everybody in all places! It was observed that hospitals can be used to confine people... for the treatment of criminals. This did not mean, necessarily, medical treatment. At that... at that time, I did not know the word *"Psycho-Prison"* as in the Soviet Union, but without trying to recall all the details, basically, he was describing the use of hospitals both for treating the sick and for confinement of criminals for reasons other than the medical well-being of the criminal. The definition of criminal was not given.

ELIMINATION OF PRIVATE DOCTORS

The image of the doctor would change. No longer would he be seen as an individual professional in service to individual patients. But the doctor would be gradually recognized as a highly skilled technician... and his job would change. The job is to include things like executions by lethal injection. The image of the doctor being a powerful, independent person would have to be changed. And he went on to say, *"Doctors are making entirely too much money. They should advertise like any other product."*

Lawyers would be advertising too. Keep in mind, this was an audience of doctors being addressed by a doctor. And it was interesting that he would make some rather insulting statements to his audience without fear of antagonizing us. The solo practitioner would become a thing of the past. A few die-hards might try to hold out, but most doctors would be employed by an institution of one kind or another. Group practice would be encouraged, corporations would be encouraged, and then once the corporate image of medical care... as this gradually became more and more acceptable, doctors would more and more become employees rather than independent contractors. And along with that, of course, unstated but necessary, is the employee serves his employer, not his patient.

So that's... we've already seen quite a lot of that in the last 20 years. And apparently more on the horizon. The term HMO was not used at that time, but as you look at HMOs you see this is the way that medical care is being taken over since the National Health Insurance approach did not get through the Congress. A few die-hard doctors may try to make a go of it; remaining in solo practice, remaining independent, which, parenthetically, is me. But they would suffer a great loss of income. They'd be able to scrape by, maybe, but never really live comfortably as would those who were willing to become employees of the system. Ultimately, there would be no room at all for the solo practitioner, after the system is entrenched.

NEW DIFFICULT TO DIAGNOSE AND UNTREATABLE DISEASES

Next heading to talk about is HEALTH & DISEASE. He said there would be new diseases to appear which had not ever been seen before. Would be very difficult to diagnose and be untreatable — at least for a long time. No elaboration was made on this, but I remember, not long after hearing this presentation, when I had a puzzling diagnosis to make, I would be wondering, *"Is this ... was what he was talking about? Is this a case of what he was talking about?"*. Some years later, as AIDS ultimately developed, I think AIDS was at least one example of what he was talking about. I now think that AIDS probably was a manufactured disease.

SUPPRESSING CANCER CURES AS A MEANS OF POPULATION CONTROL... CANCER.

He said, *"We can cure almost every cancer right now. Information is on file in the Rockefeller Institute, if it's ever decided that it should be released. But consider - if people stop dying of cancer, how rapidly we would become overpopulated. You may as well die of cancer as something else."*

Efforts at cancer treatment would be geared more toward comfort than toward cure. There was some statement ultimately the cancer cures which were being hidden in the Rockefeller Institute would come to light because independent researchers might bring them out, despite these efforts to suppress them. But at least for the time being, letting people die of cancer was a good thing to do because it would slow down the problem of overpopulation.

INDUCING HEART ATTACKS AS A FORM OF ASSASSINATION

Another very interesting thing was heart attacks. He said, *"There is now a way to simulate a real heart attack. It can be used as a means of assassinates."*

Only a very skilled pathologist who knew exactly what to look for at an autopsy, could distinguish this from the real thing. I thought that was a very surprising and shocking thing to hear from this particular man at that particular time. This, and the business of the cancer cure, really still stand out sharply in my memory, because they were so shocking and, at that time, seemed to me out of character.

He then went on to talk about nutrition and exercise, sort of in the same framework. People would not have to... people would have to eat right and exercise right to live as long as before. Most won't. This, in the connection of nutrition, there was no specific statement that I can recall as to particular nutrients that would be either inadequate or in excess. In retrospect, I tend to think he meant high salt diets and high fat diets would predispose toward high blood pressure and premature arteriosclerotic heart disease. And that if people who were too dumb or too lazy to exercise as they should then their dietary... their circulating fats go up and predispose to disease.

And he said something about diet information — about proper diet — would be widely available, but most people – particularly stupid people, who had no right to continue living anyway – they would ignore the advice and just go on and eat what was convenient and tasted good. There were some other unpleasant things said about food. I just can't recall what they were. But I do remember of... having reflections about wanting to plant a garden in the backyard to get around whatever these contaminated foods would be. I regret I don't remember the details... the rest of this... about nutrition and hazardous nutrition.

With regard to Exercise. He went on to say that more people would be exercising more, especially running, because everybody can run. You don't need any special equipment or place. You can run wherever you are. As he put it, *"people will be running all over the place."* And in this vein, he pointed out how supply produces demand. And this was in reference to athletic clothing and equipment. As this would be made more widely available and glamorized, particularly as regards running shoes, this would stimulate people to develop an interest in running and – as part of a whole sort of public propaganda campaign – people would be encouraged then to buy the attractive sports equipment and to get into exercise

Again... well in connection with nutrition he also mentioned that public eating places would rapidly increase. That... this had a connection with the family too. As more and more people eat out, eating at home would become less important. People would be less dependent on their kitchens at home. And then this also connected to convenience foods being made widely available – things like you could pop into the microwave. Whole meals would be available pre-fixed. And of course, we've now seen this... and some pretty good ones.

But this whole different approach to eating out and to previously prepared meals being eaten in the home was predicted at that time to be brought about – convenience foods. The convenience foods would be part of the hazards. Anybody who was lazy enough to want the convenience foods rather than fixing his own also had better be energetic enough to exercise. Because if he was too lazy to exercise and too lazy to fix his own food, then he didn't deserve to live very long.

This was all presented as sort of a moral judgment about people and what they should do with their energies. People who are smart, who would learn about nutrition, and who are disciplined enough to eat right and exercise right are better people – and the kind you want to live longer.

EDUCATION AS A TOOL FOR ACCELERATING THE ONSET OF PUBERTY AND EVOLUTION

Somewhere along in here there was also something about accelerating the onset of puberty. And this was said in connection with health, and later in connection with education, and connecting to accelerating the process of evolutionary change. There was a statement that *"we think that we can push evolution faster and in the direction we want it to go."* I remember this only as a general statement. I don't recall if any details were given beyond that.

BLENDING ALL RELIGIONS — THE OLD RELIGIONS WILL HAVE TO GO

Another area of discussion was RELIGION. This is an avowed atheist speaking. And he said, *"Religion is not necessarily bad. A lot of people seem to need religion, with its mysteries and rituals – so they will have religion."*

But the major religions of today have to be changed because they are not compatible with the changes to come. The old religions will have to go. Especially Christianity. Once the Roman Catholic Church is brought down, the rest of Christianity will follow easily. Then a new religion can be accepted for use all over the world. It will incorporate something from all of the old ones to make it more easy for people to accept it, and feel at home in it. Most people won't be too concerned with religion. They will realize that they don't need it.

CHANGING THE BIBLE THROUGH REVISIONS OF KEY WORDS

In order to do this, the Bible will be changed. It will be rewritten to fit the new religion. Gradually, key words will be replaced with new words having various shades of meaning. Then, the meaning attached to the new word can be close to the old word. And as time goes on, other shades of meaning of that word can be emphasized, and then gradually that word replaced with another word.

I don't know if I'm making that clear. But the idea is that everything in Scripture need not be rewritten, just key words replaced by other words. And the variability in meaning attached to any word can be used as a tool to change the entire meaning of Scripture, and therefore make it acceptable to this new religion. Most people won't know the difference; and this was another one of the times where he said, *"the few who do notice the difference won't be enough to matter."*

THE CHURCHES WILL HELP

Then followed one of the most surprising statements of the whole presentation: He said, *"some of you probably think the churches won't stand for this,"* and he went on to say, *"The churches will help us!"*

There was no elaboration on this; it was unclear just what he had in mind when he said, *"the churches will help us!"* In retrospect, I think some of us now can understand what he might have meant at that time. I recall then only of thinking, *"no they won't!"* and remembering our Lord's words where he said to Peter, *"Thou art Peter and upon this rock I will build my Church, and gates of Hell will not prevail against it."*

So... yes, some people in the churches might help. And in the subsequent 20 years we've seen how some people in churches have helped. But we also know that our Lord's Words will stand, and the gates of Hell will NOT prevail.

RESTRUCTURING EDUCATION AS A TOOL OF INDOCTRINATION

Another area of discussion was Education. And one of the things in connection with education that I remember connecting with what he said about religion, was – in addition to changing the Bible – he said that the classics in Literature would be changed. I seem to recall Mark Twain's writings was given as one example. But he said, the casual reader reading a revised version of a classic would never even suspect that there was any change. And, somebody would have to go through word by word to even recognize that any change was made in these classics; the changes would be so subtle. But the changes would be such as to promote the acceptability of the new system.

MORE TIME IN SCHOOLS, BUT THEY "WOULDN'T LEARN ANYTHING."

As regards education, he indicated that kids would spend more time in schools, but in many schools they wouldn't learn anything. They'll learn some things, but not as much as formerly. Better schools in better areas with better people – their kids will learn more. In the better schools, learning would be accelerated. And this is another time where he said, "We think we can push evolution."

By pushing kids to learn more, he seemed to be suggesting that their brains would evolve, that their offspring would evolve – sort of pushing evolution – where kids would learn and be more intelligent at a younger age. As if this pushing would alter their physiology. Overall, schooling would be prolonged. This meant prolonged through the school year. I'm not sure what he said about a long school day, I do remember he said that school was planned to go all summer, that the summer school vacation would become a thing of the past. Not only for schools, but for other reasons. People would begin to think of vacation times year round, not just in the summer.

For most people, it would take longer to complete their education. To get what originally had been in a bachelor's program would now require advanced degrees and more schooling. So that a lot of school time would be just wasted time. Good schools would become more competitive. I inferred when he said that, that he was including all schools – elementary up through college – but I don't recall whether he said that.

Students would have to decide at a younger age what they would want to study and get onto their track early, if they would qualify. It would be harder to change to another field of study once you get started. Studies would be concentrated in much greater depth, but narrowed. You wouldn't have access to material in other fields, outside your own area of study, without approval. This seems to be more... where he talked about limited access to other fields... I seem to recall that as being more at the college level, high school and college level, perhaps. People would be very specialized in their own area of expertise. But they won't be able to get a broad education and won't be able to understand what is going on overall.

CONTROLLING WHO HAS ACCESS TO INFORMATION

He was already talking about computers in education, and at that time he said anybody who wanted computer access, or access to books that were not directly related to their field of study would have to have a very good reason for so doing. Otherwise, access would be denied.

SCHOOLS AS THE HUB OF THE COMMUNITY

Another angle was that the schools would become more important in people's overall life. Kids in addition to their academics, would have to get into school activities unless they wanted to feel completely out of it. But spontaneous activities among kids – the thing that came to my mind when I heard this was sandlot football and sandlot baseball teams that we worked up as kids growing up. I said the kids wanting any activities outside of school would be almost forced to get them through the school. There would be few opportunities outside.

Now the pressures of the accelerated academic program, the accelerated demands, where kids would feel they had to be part of something – one or another athletic club or some school activity – these pressures he recognized would cause some students to burn out. He said, *"the smartest ones will learn how to cope with pressures and to survive. There will be some help available to students in handling stress, but the unfit won't be able to make it. They will then move on to other things."*

In this connection, and later on in the connection with drug abuse and alcohol abuse, he indicated that psychiatric services to help would be increased dramatically. In all the pushing for achievement, it was recognized that many people would need help, and the people worth keeping around would be able to accept and benefit from that help, and still be super-achievers. Those who could not would fall by the wayside and therefore were sort of dispensable – *"expendable"* – I guess is the word I want.

Education would be lifelong. Adults would be going to school. There'll always be new information that adults must have to keep up. When you can't keep up anymore, you're too old. This was another way of letting older people know that the time had come for them to move on and take the demise pill. If you get too tired to keep up with your education, or you got too old to learn new information, then this was a signal – you begin to prepare to get ready to step aside.

SOME BOOKS WOULD JUST DISAPPEAR FROM THE LIBRARIES

In addition to revising the classics, which I alluded to a while ago - with revising the Bible, he said, *"some books would just disappear from the libraries."*

This was in the vein that some books contain information or contain ideas that should not be kept around. And therefore, those books would disappear. I don't remember exactly if he said how this was to be accomplished. But I seem to recall carrying away this idea that this would include thefts. That certain people would be designated to go to certain libraries and pick up certain books and just get rid of them. Not necessarily as a matter of policy – just simply steal it. Further down the line, not everybody will be allowed to own books. And some books NOBODY will be allowed to own.

CHANGING LAWS

Another area of discussion was laws that would be changed. At that time a lot of States had blue laws about Sunday sales, certain Sunday activities. He said the blue laws would all be repealed. Gambling laws would be repealed or relaxed, so that gambling would be increased. He indicated then that governments would get into gambling. We've had a lot of state lotteries pop up around the country since then. And, at the time, we were already being told that would be the case. *"Why should all that gambling money be kept in private hands when the State would benefit from it?"* was the rationale behind it. But people should be able to gamble if they want to. So it would become a civil activity, rather than a private, or illegal activity.

Bankruptcy laws would be changed. I don't remember the details, but just that they would be changed. And I know subsequent to that time they have been. Antitrust laws would be changed, or be interpreted differently, or both. In connection with the changing anti-trust laws, there was some statement that in a sense, competition would be increased. But this would be increased competition within otherwise controlled circumstances. So it's not a free competition. I recall of having the impression that it was like competition but within members of a club. There would be nobody outside the club would be able to compete. Sort of like teams competing within a professional league... if you're the NFL or the American or National Baseball Leagues, you compete within the league but the league is all in agreement on what the rules of competition are – not a really free competition.

ENCOURAGEMENT OF DRUG ABUSE TO CREATE A JUNGLE ATMOSPHERE

Drug use would be increased. Alcohol use would be increased. Law enforcement efforts against drugs would be increased. On first hearing that, it sounded like a contradiction. Why increase drug abuse and simultaneously increase law enforcement against drug abuse? But the idea is that, in part, the increased availability of drugs would provide a sort of law of the jungle whereby the weak and the unfit would be selected out. There was a statement made at the time: *"Before the earth was overpopulated, there was a law of the jungle where only the fittest survived."*

You had to be able to protect yourself against the elements and wild animals and disease. And if you were fit, you survived. But now we've become so civilized – we're over civilized – and the unfit are enabled to survive, only at the expense of those who are more fit. And the abusive drugs then, would restore, in a certain sense, the law of the jungle, and selection of the fittest for survival. News about drug abuse and law enforcement efforts would tend to keep drugs in the public consciousness. And would also tend to reduce this unwarranted American complacency that the world is a safe place, and a nice place.

ALCOHOL ABUSE

The same thing would happen with alcohol. Alcohol abuse would be both promoted and demoted at the same time. The vulnerable and the weak would respond to the promotions and, therefore, use and abuse more alcohol. Drunk driving would become more of a problem; and stricter rules about driving under the influence would be established so that more and more people would lose their privilege to drive.

RESTRICTIONS ON TRAVEL

This also had connection with something we'll get to later about overall restrictions on travel. Not everybody should be free to travel the way they do now in the United States. People don't have a need to travel that way. It's a privilege! It was a kind of a high-handed way it was put. Again, much more in the way of psychological services would be made available to help those who got hooked on drugs and alcohol.

The idea being, that in order to promote this – drug and alcohol abuse to screen out some of the unfit people who are otherwise pretty good – would also be subject to getting hooked. And if they were really worth their salt they would have enough sense to seek psychological counseling and to benefit from it. So this was presented as sort of a redeeming value on the part of the planners. It was as if he were saying, *"you think we're bad in promoting these evil things — but look how nice we are – we're also providing a way out!"*

THE NEED FOR MORE JAILS, AND USING HOSPITALS AS JAILS

More jails would be needed. Hospitals could serve as jails. Some new hospital construction would be designed so as to make them adaptable to jail-like use.

Source/Reference: U.S. Coalition for Life; Box 315, Export, Penn 15632

Twenty-Two

This is a transcript of the second of three tapes on the "New Order of Barbarians", referred to on the tapes simply as the "New World System." Tapes one and two, done in 1988, are the reminiscences of Dr. Lawrence Dunegan M.D., a pediatrician from Pittsburgh, who sat through a talk in 1969, while insider, Dr. Richard Day M.D., spoke of the planned future of America and Americans. Dr. Day was speaking to a group of Pediatric Physicians who were told, *"No note-taking and no tape recorders."*

CHANGE

Change, nothing is permanent. Streets would be rerouted, renamed. Areas you had not seen in a while would become unfamiliar. Among other things, this would contribute to older people feeling that it was time to move on, they feel they couldn't even keep up with the changes in areas that were once familiar. Buildings would be allowed to stand empty and deteriorate, and streets would be allowed to deteriorate in certain localities. The purpose of this was to provide the jungle, the depressed atmosphere for the unfit. Somewhere in this same connection he mentioned that buildings and bridges would be made so that they would collapse after a while; there would be more accidents involving airplanes and railroads and automobiles. All of this to contribute to the feeling of insecurity, that nothing was safe.

Not too long after this presentation, and I think one or two even before in the area where I live, we had some newly constructed bridge to break; another newly constructed bridge defect discovered before it broke, and I remember reading just scattered incidents around the country where shopping malls would fall in – right where they were filled with shoppers. And I remember that one of the shopping malls in our area, the first building I'd ever been in where you could feel this vibration throughout the entire building when there were a lot of people in there; and I remember wondering at that time whether this shopping mall was one of the buildings he was talking about. Talking to construction people and architects about it they would say, "Oh no, that's good when the building vibrates like that. That means it's flexible, not rigid." Well... maybe so. We'll wait and see.

Other areas there would be well-maintained. Not every part of the city would be slums. There would be the created slums and other areas well-maintained. Those people able to leave the slums for better areas then would learn to better appreciate the importance of human accomplishment. This meant that if they left the jungle and came to civilization, so to speak, they could be proud of their own accomplishments that they made it. There was no related sympathy for those who were left behind in the jungle of drugs and deteriorating neighborhoods. Then a statement that was kind of surprising: *"We think we can effectively limit crime to the slum areas, so it won't be spread heavily into better areas."*

CONSOLIDATING POLICY

I should maybe point out here that these are obviously not word for word quotations after 20 years, but where I say that I am quoting, I am giving the general drift of what was said close to word for word; perhaps not precisely so. But anyhow, I remember wondering, *"How can he be so confident that the criminal element is going to stay where he wants it to stay?"* But he went on to say that increased security would be needed in the better areas.

That would mean more police, better coordinated police efforts. He did not say so, but I wondered at that time about the moves that were afoot to consolidate all the police departments of suburbs around the major cities. I think the John Birch Society was one that was saying, *"Support your local police; don't let them be consolidated."* And I remember wondering if that was one of the things he had in mind about security.

It was not explicitly stated. But anyhow, he went on to say there would be a whole new industry of residential security systems to develop with alarms and locks and alarms going into the police department so that people could protect their wealth and their wellbeing. Because some of the criminal activity would spill out of the slums into better, more affluent looking areas that looked like they would be worth burglarizing. And again it was stated like it was a redeeming quality. *"See, we're generating all this more crime, but look how good we are – we're also generating the means for you to protect yourself against the crime."* A sort of repeated thing throughout this presentation was the recognized evil and then the self-forgiveness thing... *"Well see, we've given you a way out."*

GLOBAL INTERDEPENDENCE "TO CREATE A NEW STRUCTURE, YOU FIRST HAVE TO TEAR DOWN THE OLD"

American industry came under discussion – it was the first that I'd heard the term GLOBAL INTERDEPENDENCE or that notion. The stated plan was that different parts of the world would be assigned different roles of industry and commerce in a unified global system. The continued pre-eminence of the United States and the relative independence and self-sufficiency of the United States would have to be changed. This was one of the several times that he said in order to create a new structure, you first have to tear down the old, and American industry was one example of that. Our system would have to be curtailed in order to give other countries a chance to build their industries, because otherwise they would not be able to compete against the United States. And this was especially true of our heavy industries that would be cut back while the same industries were being developed in other countries, notably Japan.

PATRIOTISM WOULD GO DOWN THE DRAIN

And at this point there was some discussion of steel and particularly automobiles. I remember him saying that automobiles would be imported from Japan on an equal footing with our own domestically produced automobiles, but the Japanese product would be better. Things would be made so they would break and fall apart – that is, in the United States – so that people would tend to prefer the imported variety and this would give a bit of a boost to foreign competitors. One example, was Japanese. In 1969, Japanese automobiles – if they were sold here at all, I don't remember – but they certainly weren't very popular.

But the idea was, you could get a little bit disgusted with your Ford, GM, or Chrysler product – or whatever – because little things like window handles would fall off more, and plastic parts would break which, had they been made of metal, would hold up. Your patriotism about buying American would soon give way to practicality that if you bought Japanese, German, or imported that it would last longer and you would be better off. Patriotism would go down the drain then.

It was mentioned elsewhere, things being made to fall apart too. I don't remember specific items or if they were even stated other than automobiles, but I do recall of having the impression, sort of in my imagination, of a surgeon having something fall apart in his hands in the operating room, at a critical time. Was he including this sort of thing in his discussion? But somewhere in this discussion about things being made deliberately defective and unreliable not only was to tear down patriotism but to be just a little source of irritation to people who would use such things.

LOSS OF JOBS — LOSS OF SECURITY

Again, the idea that you not feel terribly secure, promoting the notion that the world isn't a terribly reliable place. The United States was to be kept strong in information, communications, high technology, education and agriculture. The United States was seen as continuing to be sort of the keystone of this global system. But heavy industry would be transported out. One of the comments made about heavy industry was that we had had enough environmental damage from smokestacks and industrial waste and some of the other people could put up with that for a while. This again, was supposed to be a "redeeming quality" for Americans to accept. You took away our industry but you saved our environment. So we really didn't lose on it.

POPULATION SHIFTS TO ELIMINATE "TRADITIONS"

And along this line there were talks about people losing their jobs as a result of industry and opportunities for retraining, and particularly population shifts would be brought about. This is sort of an aside. I think I'll explore the aside before I forget it. Population shifts were to be brought about so that people would be tending to move into the Sun Belt. They would be, sort of, people without roots in their new locations, and traditions are easier to change in a place where there are a lot of transplanted people, as compared to trying to changing traditions in a place where people grew up and had an extended family – where they had roots. Things like new medical care systems. If you pick up from a Northeast industrial city and you transplant yourself to the South Sun Belt or Southwest, you'll be more accepting of whatever kind of, for example, controlled medical care you find there than you would accept a change in the medical care system where you had roots and the support of your family. Also in this vein it was mentioned – he used the plural personal pronoun *"we"* – we take control first of the port cities... New York, San Francisco, Seattle... the idea being that this is a piece of strategy. The idea being that if you control the port cities with your philosophy and your way of life, the HEARTLAND in between has to yield.

I can't elaborate more on that but it is interesting, if you look around the most liberal areas of the country – and progressively so – are the seacoast cities; the heartland, the Midwest, does seem to have maintained its conservatism. But as you take away industry and jobs and relocate people then this is a strategy to break down conservatism. When you take away industry, and people are unemployed and poor they will accept whatever change seems to offer them survival; and their morals and their commitment to things will all give way to survival. That's not my philosophy. That's the speaker's philosophy.

WORLD CITIZENS — WORLD SPORTS

Anyhow, going back to industry. Some heavy industry would remain. Just enough to maintain a sort of a seedbed of industrial skills which could be expanded if the plan didn't work out as it was intended. So the country would not be devoid of assets and skills. But this was just sort of a contingency plan. It was hoped and expected that the worldwide specialization would be carried on.

But, perhaps repeating myself, one of the upshots of all of this is that with this global interdependence then national identities would tend to be de-emphasized. Each area depended on every other area for one or another elements in its life. We would all become citizens of the world rather than citizens of any one country.

And along these lines then we can talk about sports. Sports in the United States was to be changed, in part as a way of de-emphasizing nationalism. Soccer, a world-wide sport, was to be emphasized and pushed in the United States and this was of interest because in this area the game of soccer was virtually unknown at that time. I had a few friends who attended an elementary school other than the one I attended where they played soccer at their school, and they were a real novelty. This was back in the 50's. So to hear this man speak of soccer in this area was kind of surprising.

Anyhow, soccer is seen as an international sport and would be promoted and the traditional sport of American baseball would be de-emphasized and possibly eliminated because it might be seen as too American. And he discussed eliminating this. One's first reaction would be *well, they pay the players poorly and they don't want to play for poor pay so they give up baseball and either go into some other sport or some other activity.* But, he said that's really not how it works. Actually, the way to break down baseball would be to make the salaries go very high.

The idea behind this was that as the salaries got ridiculously high there would be a certain amount of discontent and antagonism as people resented the athletes being paid so much, and the athletes would begin more and more to resent among themselves what other players were paid and would tend to abandon the sport. And these high salaries then also could break the owners and alienate the fans. And then the fans would support soccer and the baseball fields could be used as soccer fields. It wasn't said definitely this would have to happen, but if the international flavor didn't come around rapidly enough this could be done.

There was some comment along the same lines about football, although I seem to recall he said football would be harder to dismantle because it was so widely played in colleges as well as in the professional leagues and would be harder to tear down. There was something else also about the violence in football that met a psychological need that was perceived, and people have a need for this vicarious violence. So football, for that reason, might be left around to meet that vicarious need.

The same thing is true of hockey. Hockey had more of an inter-national flavor and would be emphasized. There was some foreseeable international competition about hockey and particularly soccer. At that time hockey was international between the United States and Canada. I was kind of surprised because I thought the speaker just never impressed me as being at all a hockey fan, and I am. And it turns out, he was not. He just knew about the game and what it would do to this changing sports program.

But in any event soccer was to be the keystone of athletics because it is already a world-wide sport in South America, in Europe, in parts of Asia and the United States should get on the bandwagon. All this would foster international competition so that we would all become citizens of the world to a greater extent than citizens of our narrow nations.

HUNTING

There was some discussion about hunting, not surprisingly. Hunting requires guns and gun control is a big element in these plans. I don't remember the details much, but the idea is that gun ownership is a privilege and not everybody should have guns. Hunting was an inadequate excuse for owning guns and everybody should be restricted in gun ownership. The few privileged people who should be allowed to hunt could maybe rent or borrow a gun from official quarters rather than own their own. After all, everybody doesn't have a need for a gun, is the way it was put.

SPORTS FOR GIRLS — TO DE-EMPHASIZE FEMININITY

Very important in sports was sports for girls. Athletics would be pushed for girls. This was intended to replace dolls. Baby dolls would still be around, a few of them, but you would not see the number and variety of dolls. Dolls would not be pushed because girls should not be thinking about babies and reproduction. Girls should be out on the athletic field just as the boys are. Girls and boys really need not to be all that different. Tea sets were to go the way of dolls, and all these things that traditionally were thought of as feminine would be de-emphasized as girls got into more masculine pursuits.

Just one other thing I recall was that the sports pages would be full of the scores of girl's teams just right along there with the boy's teams. And that's recently begun to appear after 20 years in our local papers. The girl's sports scores are right along with the boy's sports scores. So all of this to change the role model of what young girls should look to be. While she's growing up she should look to be an athlete rather to look forward to being a mother.

ENTERTAINMENT: VIOLENCE, SEX AND MORE SEX DESENSITIZATION — PREPARING THE PEOPLE FOR "HUMAN CASUALTIES"

Movies would gradually be made more explicit as regards sex and language. After all, sex and rough language are real and why pretend that they are not? There would be pornographic movies in the theaters, on television. And VCR's were not around at that time, but he had indicated that these cassettes would be available, and video cassette players would be available for use in the home and pornographic movies would be available for use on these VCRs as well as in the neighborhood theater and on your television. He said something like, *"You'll see people in the movies doing everything you can think of."*

He went on to say that... and all of this is intended to bring sex out in the open. That was another comment that was made several times – the term *"sex out in the open."* Violence would be made more graphic. This was intended to desensitize people to violence. There might need to be a time when people would witness real violence and be a part of it. Later on it will become clear where this is headed. So there would be more realistic violence in entertainment which would make it easier for people to adjust.

People's attitudes towards death would change and they would not be so fearful of it but more accepting of it, and not be so aghast at the sight of dead people or injured people. We don't need to have a genteel population paralyzed by what they might see. People would just learn to say, *"well, I don't want that to happen to me."*

This was the first statement suggesting that the plan includes numerous human casualties which the survivors would see. This particular aspect of the presentation came back in my memory very sharply a few years later when a movie about the Lone Ranger came out and I took my very young son to see it and early in the movie were some very violent scenes. One of the victims was shot in the forehead and there was sort of a splat where the bullet entered his forehead and blood and I remember regretting that I took my son, and remember feeling anger toward the doctor who spoke. Not that he made the movie, but he agreed to be part of this movement, and I was repelled by the movie and it brought back this aspect of his presentation very sharply in my memory.

MUSIC WILL GET WORSE

As regards music, he made a rather straightforward statement like, *"Music will get worse."* In 1969, Rock music was getting more and more unpleasant. It was interesting just his words the way he expressed it. It would "get worse"... acknowledging that it was already bad. Lyrics would become more openly sexual. No new sugary romantic music would be publicized like that which had been written before that time.

All of the old music would be brought back on certain radio stations and records for older people to here. And all the folks would have sort of their own radio stations to hear. Younger people, as it got worse and worse, he seemed to indicate that one group would not hear the other group's music. Older folks would just refuse to hear the junk that was offered to young people, and the young people would accept the junk because it identified them as their generation and helped them feel distinct from the older generation.

I remember at the time thinking that would not last very long because even young kids wouldn't like the junk when they got a chance to hear the older music that was prettier they would gravitate toward it. Unfortunately, I was wrong about that, when the kids get through their teens and into their 20's some of them improve their taste in music, but unfortunately he was right. They get used to this junk and that's all they want. A lot of them can't stand really pretty music. He went on to say that the music would carry a message to the young and nobody would even know the message was there. They would just think it was loud music. At the time, I didn't understand quite what he meant by that, but in retrospect, I think we know now what the messages are in the music for the young.

GIVE US THE YOUNG

And again, he was right. This aspect was sort of summarized with the notion that entertainment would be a tool to influence young people. It won't change the older people, they are already set in their ways, but the changes would be all aimed at the young, who are in their formative years, and the older generation would be passing. Not only could you not change them, but they are relatively unimportant, anyhow. Once they live out their lives and are gone, the younger generation being formed, are the ones that would be important for the future in the 21st century.

He also indicated all the old movies would be brought back again, and I remember on hearing that through my mind ran quickly the memories of a number of old movies. I wondered if they would be included, the ones that I thought I would like to see again.

Along with bringing back old music and old movies for older people there were other privileges that would also be accorded older folks: free transportation, breaks on purchases, discounts, tax discounts – a number of privileges just because they were older. This was stated to be sort of a reward for the generation which had grown up through the depression and had survived the rigors of World War II. They had deserved it, and they were going to be rewarded with all these goodies, and the bringing back of the good old music and the good old movies was going to help ease them through their final years in comfort.

'80s AND '90s — THE GRIM REAPER. TRAVEL RESTRICTIONS — NATIONAL ID — THE CHIP, ETC.

Then, the presentation began to get rather grim, because once that generation passed, and that would be in the late 80's and early 90's where we are now, most of that [age] group would be gone and then, gradually, things would tighten up and the tightening up would be accelerated. The old movies and old songs would be withdrawn; the gentler entertainment would be withdrawn. Travel, instead of being easy for old folks... travel then would become very restricted. People would need permission to travel and they would need a good reason to travel. If you didn't have a good reason for your travel you would not be allowed to travel, and everyone would need ID.

This would at first be an ID card you would carry on your person and you must show when you are asked for it. It was already planned that later on some sort of device would be developed to be implanted under the skin that would be coded specifically to identify the individual. This would eliminate the possibility of false ID and also eliminate the possibility of people saying, *"Well, I lost my ID."*

The difficulty about these skin-implanted ID was stated to be getting material that would stay in or under the skin without causing foreign body reaction whereby the body would reject it or cause infection, and that this would have to be material on which information could be recorded and retrieved by some sort of scanner while it was not rejected by the body.

Silicon was mentioned. Silicon at that time was thought to be well tolerated. It was used to augment breasts. Women who felt their breasts were too small would get silicone implants, and I guess that still goes on. At any rate silicon was seen at that time as the promising material to do both... to be retained in the body without rejection and to be able to retain information retrievable by electronic means.

FOOD CONTROL

Food supplies would come under tight control. If population growth didn't slow down, food shortages could be created in a hurry and people would realize the dangers of overpopulation. Ultimately, whether the population slows down or not the food supply is to be brought under centralized control so that people would have enough to be well-nourished but they would not have enough to support any fugitive from the new system. In other words, if you had a friend or relative who didn't sign on [side one ends abruptly continue on side two]

And growing one's own food would be outlawed. This would be done under some sort of pretext. In the beginning, I mentioned there were two purposes for everything – one the ostensible purpose and one the real purpose – and the ostensible purpose here would be that growing your own vegetables was unsafe, it would spread disease or something like that.

So the acceptable idea was to protect the consumer but the real idea was to limit the food supply and growing your own food would be illegal.

And if you persist in illegal activities like growing your own food, then you're a criminal.

WEATHER CONTROL

There was a mention then of weather. This was another really striking statement. He said, *"We can or soon will be able to control the weather."*

He said, *"I'm not merely referring to dropping iodide crystals into the clouds to precipitate rain that's already there, but REAL control."* And weather was seen as a weapon of war, a weapon of influencing public policy. It could make rain or withhold rain in order to influence certain areas and bring them under your control. There were two sides to this that were rather striking.

He said, *"On the one hand you can make drought during the growing season so that nothing will grow, and on the other hand you can make for very heavy rains during harvest season so the fields are too muddy to bring in the harvest, and indeed one might be able to do both."*

There was no statement how this would be done. It was stated that either it was already possible or very close to being possible.

POLITICS

He said that very few people really know how government works. Something to the effect that elected officials are influenced in ways that they don't even realize, and they carry out plans that have been made for them, and they think that they are authors of the plans. But actually they are manipulated in ways they don't understand.

KNOW HOW PEOPLE RESPOND — MAKING THEM DO WHAT YOU WANT

Somewhere in the presentation he made two statements that I want to insert at this time. I don't remember just where they were made, but they're valid in terms of the general overall view. One statement: *"People can carry in their minds and act upon two contradictory ideas at one time, provided that these two contradictory ideas are kept far enough apart."*

And the other statement is, *"You can know pretty well how rational people are going to respond to certain circumstances or to certain information that they encounter. So, to determine the response you want, you need only control the kind of data or information that they're presented or the kinds of circumstance that they're in; and being rational people they'll do what you want them to do. They may not fully understand what they're doing or why."*

FALSIFIED SCIENTIFIC RESEARCH

Somewhere in this connection, then, was the statement admitting that some scientific research data could be – and indeed HAS been – falsified in order to bring about desired results. And here was said, *"People don't ask the right questions. Some people are too trusting."*

Now this was an interesting statement because the speaker and the audience all being doctors of medicine and supposedly very objectively, dispassionately scientific and science being the be all and end-all... well to falsify scientific research data in that setting is like blasphemy in the church... you just don't do that. Anyhow, out of all of this was to come the New International Governing Body, probably to come through the UN and with a World Court, but not necessarily through those structures. It could be brought about in other ways.

ACCEPTANCE OF THE U.N. — THE END JUSTIFIES THE MEANS

Acceptance of the U.N. at that time was seen as not being as wide as was hoped. Efforts would continue to give the United Nations increasing importance. People would be more and more used to the idea of relinquishing some national sovereignty. Economic interdependence would foster this goal from a peaceful standpoint.

Avoidance of war would foster it from the standpoint of worrying about hostilities. It was recognized that doing it peaceably was better than doing it by war. It was stated at this point that war was *"obsolete."* I thought that was an interesting phrase because obsolete means something that once was seen as useful is no longer useful. But war is obsolete... this being because of the nuclear bombs war is no longer controllable.

Formerly, wars could be controlled, but if nuclear weapons would fall into the wrong hands there could be an unintended nuclear disaster. It was not stated who the "wrong hands" are. We were free to infer that maybe this meant terrorists, but in more recent years I'm wondering whether the wrong hands might also include people that we've assumed that they've had nuclear weapons all along... maybe they don't have them.

Just as it was stated that industry would be preserved in the United States – a little bit, just in case the world wide plans didn't work out; just in case some country or some other powerful person decided to bolt from the pack and go his own way – one wonders whether this might also be true with nuclear weapons. When you hear that... he said they might fall into the wrong hands, there was some statement that the possession of nuclear weapons had been tightly controlled, sort of implying that anybody who had nuclear weapons was intended to have them. That would necessarily have included the Soviet Union, if indeed they have them.

But I recall wondering at the time, *"Are you telling us, or are you implying that this country willingly gave weapons to the Soviets?"* At that time that seemed like a terribly unthinkable thing to do, much less to admit. The leaders of the Soviet Union seem to be so dependent on the West though, one wonders whether there may have been some fear that they would try to assert independence if they indeed had these weapons. So, I don't know. It's something to speculate about perhaps... Who did he mean when he said, *"If these weapons fall into the wrong hands"?* Maybe just terrorists.

Anyhow, the new system would be brought in, if not by peaceful co-operation – everybody willingly yielding national sovereignty – then by bringing the nation to the brink of nuclear war. And everybody would be so fearful as hysteria is created by the possibility of nuclear war that there would be a strong public outcry to negotiate a public peace and people would willingly give up national sovereignty in order to achieve peace, and thereby this would bring in the New International Political System.

This was stated and very impressive thing to hear then... "If there were too many people in the right places who resisted this, there might be a need to use one or two – possibly more – nuclear weapons. As it was put this would be possibly needed to convince people that *"We mean business"*.

That was followed by the statement that, *"By the time one or two of those went off then everybody – even the most reluctant – would yield."*

He said something about *"this negotiated peace would be very convincing,"* as kind of in a framework or in a context that the whole thing was rehearsed but nobody would know it. People hearing about it would be convinced that it was a genuine negotiation between hostile enemies who finally had come to the realization that peace was better than war.

WAR IS GOOD — YOU GET TO BE CANNON-FODDER, KEEP THE POPULATION DOWN, AND DIE A HERO

In this context discussing war, and war is obsolete, a statement was made that there were some good things about war... one, you're going to die anyway, and people sometimes in war get a chance to display great courage and heroism and if they die they've died well and if they survive they get recognition. So that in any case, the hardships of war on soldiers are worth it because that's the reward they get out of their warring.

Another justification expressed for war was, if you think of the many millions of casualties in WWI and WWII, well... suppose all those people had not died but had continued to live, then continued to have babies. There would be millions upon millions and we would already be overpopulated, so those two great wars served a benign purpose in delaying over-population. But now there are technological means for the individual and governments to control over-population so in this regard war is obsolete. It's no longer needed. And then again, it's obsolete because nuclear weapons could destroy the whole universe. War, which once was controllable, could get out of control and so for these two reasons it's now obsolete.

TERRORISM — THE GREAT TOOL FOR 'CONTROL'

There was a discussion of terrorism. Terrorism would be used widely in Europe and in other parts of the world. Terrorism at that time was thought would not be necessary in the United States. It could become necessary in the United States if the United States did not move rapidly enough into accepting the system. But at least in the foreseeable future it was not planned. And very benignly on their part. Maybe terrorism would not be required here, but the implication being that it would be indeed used if it was necessary.

Along with this came a bit of a scolding that Americans had had it too good anyway and just a little bit of terrorism would help convince Americans that the world is indeed a dangerous place... or can be if we don't relinquish control to the proper authorities.

MONEY AND BANKING

There was discussion of money and banking. One statement was, *"Inflation is infinite. You can put an infinite number of zeros after any number and put the decimals points wherever you want"*, as an indication that inflation is a TOOL of the controllers.

Money would become predominately credit. It was already... money is primarily a credit thing, but exchange of money would be not cash or palpable things but electronic credit signal. People would carry money only in very small amounts for things like chewing gum and candy bars. Just pocket sorts of things. Any purchase of any significant amount would be done electronically. Earnings would be electronically entered into your account.

It would be a single banking system. [It] may have the appearance of being more than one but ultimately and basically it would be one single banking system, so that when you got paid your pay would be entered for you into your account balance and then when you purchased anything at the point of purchase it would be deducted from your account balance and you would actually carry nothing with you.

Also computer records can be kept on whatever it was you purchased so that if you were purchasing too much of any particular item and some official wanted to know what you were doing with your money they could go back and review your purchases and determine what you were buying.

There was a statement that any purchase of significant size like an automobile, bicycle, a refrigerator, a radio or television or whatever might have some sort of identification on it so it could be traced, so that very quickly anything which was either given away or stolen – whatever – authorities would be able to establish who purchased it and when.

Computers would allow this to happen. The ability to save would be greatly curtailed. People would just not be able to save any considerable degree of wealth. There was some statement of recognition that wealth represents power, and wealth in the hands of a lot of people is not good for the people in charge, so if you save too much you might be taxed. The more you save the higher rate of tax on your savings so your savings really could never get very far. And also if you began to show a pattern of saving too much, you might have your pay cut. We would say, *"Well, you're saving instead of spending. You really don't need all that money."*

That basically the idea being to prevent people from accumulating any wealth which might have long range disruptive influence on the system. People would be encouraged to use credit to borrow, and then also be encouraged to renege on their debt, so they would destroy their own credit. The idea here is that, again, if you're too stupid to handle credit wisely, this gives the authorities the opportunity to come down hard on you once you've shot your credit.

Electronic payments initially would all be based on different kinds of credit cards... these were already in use in 1969 to some extent. Not as much as now. But people would have credit cards with the electronic strip on it and once they got used to that then it would be pointed out the advantage of having all of that combined into a single credit card, serving a single monetary system and then they won't have to carry around all that plastic.

So the next step would be the single card and then the next step would be to replace the single card with a skin implant. The single card could be lost or stolen, give rise to problems; could be exchanged with somebody else to confuse identify. The skin implant on the other hand would be not losable or counterfeitable or transferrable to another person so you and your accounts would be identified without any possibility of error. And the skin implants would have to be put some place that would be convenient to the skin; for example your right hand or your forehead.

At that time when I heard this I was unfamiliar with the statements in the Book of Revelation. The speaker went on to say, *"Now some of you people who read the Bible will attach significance to this to the Bible,"* but he went on to disclaim any Biblical significance at all. This is just common sense of how the system could work and should work and there's no need to read any superstitious Biblical principles into it. As I say, at the time I was not very familiar with the words of Revelations. Shortly after, I became familiar with it and the significance of what he said really was striking. I'll never forget it.

Dr. Vic Naumov

BIG BROTHER IS WATCHING YOU, WHILE YOU'RE WATCHING TV

There was some mention, also, of implants that would lend themselves to surveillance by providing radio signals. This could be under the skin or a dental implant... put in like a filling so that either fugitives or possibly other citizens could be identified by a certain frequency from his personal transmitter and could be located at any time or any place by any authority who wanted to find him. This would be particularly useful for somebody who broke out of prison.

There was more discussion of personal surveillance. One more thing was said, *"You'll be watching television and somebody will be watching you at the same time at a central monitoring station."*

Television sets would have a device to enable this. The TV set would not have to be on in order for this to be operative. Also, the television set can be used to monitor what you are watching. People can tell what you're watching on TV and how you're reacting to what you're watching. And you would not know that you were being watched while you were watching your television.

How would we get people to accept these things into their homes? Well, people would buy them when they buy their own television. They won't know that they're on there at first. This was described by being what we now know as Cable TV to replace the antenna TV. When you buy a TV set this monitor would just be part of the set and most people would not have enough knowledge to know it was there in the beginning. And then the cable would be the means of carrying the surveillance message to the monitor. By the time people found out that this monitoring was going on, they would also be very dependent upon television for a number of things. Just the way people are dependent upon the telephone today.

One thing the television would be used for would be purchases. You wouldn't have to leave your home to purchase. You just turn on your TV and there would be a way of interacting with your television channel to the store that you wanted to purchase. And you could flip the switch from place to place to choose a refrigerator or clothing. This would be both convenient, but it would also make you dependent on your television so the built-in monitor would be something you could not do without. There was some discussion of audio monitors, too, just in case the authorities wanted to hear what was going on in rooms other than where the television monitor was, and in regard to this the statement was made, *"Any wire that went into your house, for example your telephone wire, could be used this way."*

I remember this in particular because it was fairly near the end of the presentation and as we were leaving the meeting place, I said something to one of my colleagues about going home and pulling all of the wires out of my house... except I knew I couldn't get by without the telephone. And the colleague I spoke to just seemed numb. To this day, I don't think he even remembers what we talked about or what we heard that time, cause I've asked him. But at that time he seemed stunned.

Before all these changes would take place with electronic monitoring, it was mentioned that there would be service trucks all over the place, working on the wires and putting in new cables. This is how people who were on the inside would know how things were progressing.

PRIVATELY OWNED HOMES — "A THING OF THE PAST"

Privately owned housing would become a thing of the past. The cost of housing and financing housing would gradually be made so high that most people couldn't afford it. People who already owned their houses would be allowed to keep them but as years go by it would be more and more difficult for young people to buy a house. Young people would more and more become renters, particularly in apartments or condominiums. More and more unsold houses would stand vacant. People just couldn't buy them. But the cost of housing would not come down.

You'd right away think, well the vacant house, the price would come down, the people would buy it. But there was some statement to the effect that the price would be held high even though there were many available so that free market places would not operate. People would not be able to buy these and gradually more and more of the population would be forced into small apartments… small apartments which would not accommodate very many children. Then as the number of real home-owners diminished they would become a minority.

There would be no sympathy for them from the majority who dwelled in the apartments and then these homes could be taken by increased taxes or other regulations that would be detrimental to home ownership and would be acceptable to the majority. Ultimately, people would be assigned where they would live and it would be common to have non-family members living with you. This by way of your not knowing just how far you could trust anybody. This would all be under the control of a central housing authority. Have this in mind in 1990 when they ask, *"How many bedrooms in your house? How many bathrooms in your house? Do you have a finished game room?"*.

This information is personal and is of no national interest to government under our existing Constitution. But you'll be asked those questions and decide how you want to respond to them.

When the new system takes over people will be expected to sign allegiance to it, indicating that they don't have any reservations or holding back to the old system. *"There just won't be any room", he said, "for people who won't go along. We can't have such people cluttering up the place so such people would be taken to special places,"*

And here I don't remember the exact words, but the inference I drew was that at these special places where they were taken, then they would not live very long. He may have said something like, *"disposed of humanely"*, but I don't remember very precisely... just the impression the system was not going to support them when they would not go along with the system. That would leave death as the only alternative.

Somewhere in this vein he said there would not be any martyrs. When I first heard this I thought it meant the people would not be killed, but as the presentation developed what he meant was they would not be killed in such a way or disposed of in such a way that they could serve as inspiration to other people the way martyrs do. Rather he said something like this. *"People will just disappear."*

A FEW FINAL ITEMS...

Just a few additional items sort of thrown in here in the end which I failed to include where they belong more perfectly.

One: The bringing in of the new system he said probably would occur on a weekend in the winter. Everything would shut down on Friday evening and Monday morning, when everybody wakened, there would be an announcement that the New System was in place. During the process in getting the United States ready for these changes everybody would be busier with less leisure time and less opportunity to really look about and see what was going on around them.

Also, there would be more changes and more difficulty in keeping up as far as one's investments. Investment instruments would be changing. Interest rates would be changing so that it would be a difficult job with keeping up with what you had already earned.

Interesting about automobiles; it would look as though there were many varieties of automobiles, but when you look very closely there would be great duplication. They would be made to look different with chrome and wheel covers and this sort of thing, but looking closely one would see that the same automobile was made by more than one manufacturer.

This recently was brought down to me when I was in a parking lot and saw a small Ford – I forget the model – and a small Japanese automobile which were identical except for a number of things like the number of holes in the wheel cover and the chrome around the plate and the shape of the grill. But if you looked at the basic parts of the automobile, they were identical. They just happened to be parked side-by-side, where I was struck with this, and I was again reminded of what had been said many years ago.

I'm hurrying here because I'm just about to the end of the tape. Let me just summarize here by saying, all of these things said by one individual at one time in one place relating to so many different human endeavors and then to look and see how many of these actually came about... that is, changes accomplished between then and now [1969 - 1988] and the things which are planned for the future, I think there is no denying that this is controlled and there is indeed a conspiracy.

The question then becomes what to do. I think first off, WE MUST PUT OUR FAITH IN GOD and PRAY and ASK FOR HIS GUIDANCE. And secondly, do what we can to inform other individuals as much as possible, as much as they may be interested.

SOME PEOPLE JUST DON'T CARE, because they're preoccupied with getting along in their own personal endeavors. But, as much as possible, I think we should try to inform other people who may be interested, and again...

PUT OUR FAITH AND TRUST IN GOD AND PRAY CONSTANTLY FOR HIS GUIDANCE AND FOR THE COURAGE TO ACCEPT WHAT WE MAY BE FACING IN THE NEAR FUTURE. Rather than accept PEACE and JUSTICE which we hear so much now... it's a cliché. LET'S INSIST ON LIBERTY AND JUSTICE FOR ALL.

Source/Reference: U.S. Coalition for Life; Box 315, Export, Penn 15632

Twenty-Three

1969: DR. DAY'S PREDICTIONS AND THE
NEW WORLD ORDER (PART 3)

This interview by Randy Engel, Director of the U.S. Coalition for Life, with Dr. Larry Dunegan was taped on Oct. 10, 1991 in Pittsburgh, Penn. On tapes 1 and 2, (made in 1988) Dr. Dunegan, spoke about his recollections of the lecture he attended in 1969 where Dr. Richard Day, an insider, revealed the plans for their New World System, AKA the totalitarian, socialist World Government. Once again, this final tape/interview speaks for itself.

Randy Engel (R.E.): Why don't we open up with a little bit about the man who you are talking about on these tapes. Just a little profile and a little bit about his education and particularly his relationship with the population control establishment. I think that probably was his entree into much of this information.

Dr. Lawrence Dunegan, M.D. (DLD): Yeah. Dr. Day was the Chairman of the Department of Pediatrics at the University of Pittsburgh from about 1959 thru '64, about that period of time, and then he left the

University of Pittsburgh and went to fill the position of Medical Director of Planned Parenthood Federation of America.

R.E: And that was what... about 1965 to '68, about that period?

D.L.D: About '64 or '65 'til about '68 or '69, and then he left there... I don't know specifically why, I did not know him intimately. We were, you know, more than acquainted... I was a student and he would see me at lectures and, so he knew my name as a student, probably corrected some of my test scores and that sort of thing. Of course, I knew him as lecturer - would stand in front of the auditorium and listen as he talked about diseases... and take notes.

R.E: What's interesting is that this man is not as well known, I think to our listeners as names like Mary Calderone and Allen Gootmacher. They were medical directors at one time or another for Planned Parenthood, but Dr. Day was not well known. And as a matter of fact when I went back into the SIECUS archives there was very little information that had his actual name on it. So he was not one of the better known of the medical directors, but I'd say he probably had the scoop of what was going on as well - if not better - than any of the others before or after he came. Can you describe the scene of this particular lecture, the approximate date, and what was the occasion - and then a little bit about the audience?

D.L.D: This was the... the Pittsburgh Pediatric Society holds about four meetings each year where we have some speaker come in and talk about a medical topic related to pediatrics and this was our spring meeting. It's always late February or early part of March. This was in March, 1969 and it was held at a restaurant called the Lamont which is well known in Pittsburgh. Beautiful place. In attendance, I would say somewhere in the neighborhood of 80 people. Mostly physicians, if not exclusively physicians. Predominantly pediatricians, particularly pediatric surgeons and pediatric radiologists - other people who were involved in medical care of children, even though they might not be pediatricians as such.

R.E: And the speech was given after the meal, I presume?

D.L.D: A very nice meal and everyone was settled down, quite comfortable and quite filled and really an ideal state to absorb what was coming.

R.E: But when you listen to the tape, he says some of the most... well not only outrageous things, but things you would think a pediatrician would kind of almost jump out of his seat at... for example when he mentions the cancer cures. There were probably doctors in the audience who were perhaps treating a child or knowing of a child who was in need of a particular cancer cure. And to hear that some of these prescriptions for or treatments for cancer were sitting over at the Rockefeller Institute, and yet, as far as I got from the tape everyone just kind of sat there... didn't say very much. I mean he was talking about falsifying scientific data and everyone just kind of yawns and... How long did this speech go on?

D.L.D: Two hours. He spoke for over two hours which was longer than most of our speakers go and one of the interesting things... he hasn't finished, it was getting late and he said, *"there's much much more, but we could be here all night but it's time to stop"*.

And I think that's significant, that there was much more that we never heard. In the beginning of the presentation, I don't know whether I mentioned this at the introduction of the first tape or not, but somewhere in the beginning of this he said, *"You will forget most or much of what I'm going to tell you tonight."*

And at the time I thought, well, sure, that's true. We tend to forget. You know, somebody talks for hours you forget a lot of what they say. But, there is such a thing as the power of suggestion and I can't say for sure but I do wonder if this may not have been a suggestion when we were all full of a nice dinner and relaxed and listening - we took that suggestion and forgot, because I know a number of my colleagues who were there when I would - some years later - say, *"Do you remember when Dr. Day said this, or he said that or said the other?"* They'd say, *"Well, yeah, I kind of... is that what he said? You know I kind of remember that".*

But most were not very impressed, which to me was surprising because... well use the example of cancer cures. But he said a number of things that...

R.E: Like doctors making too much money...?

D.L.D: Yeah, changing the image of the doctor. You're just going to be a high-paid technician rather than a professional who exercises independent judgment on behalf of his independent patient. A number of things that I thought should have been offensive and elicited a reaction from physicians because they were physicians. I was surprised at how little reaction there was to it. And then other things that I would have expected people to react to just because they were human beings and I think most of the people at the meeting subscribed more or less to the Judeo-Christian ethic and codes of behavior, and that was violated right and left. And particularly one of my friends I thought would be as disturbed as I was about this just sort of smiled... wasn't disturbed at a ll. I thought, gee, this is surprising.

R.E: Was part of it also because of his prominence? I mean he was...

D.L.D: The authority... Authority figure? Yeah, I think there might be something there. This is the authority. We sort of owe some deference here.

R.E: And he couldn't possibly mean what he's saying or there couldn't possibly be any... I mean, he's such a good guy.

D.L.D: I've often heard that phrase, *"He's such a good guy. I can't believe he'd actually mean the things"*... I can only speculate about this. But I do think at the time there was an element of disbelief about all of this. Thinking, well this is somebody's fairy tale plan but it will never really happen because it's too outlandish. Of course we know step by step it is indeed happening right under our feet.

R.E: Before talking about the specific areas, I think there's a lot of benefits from this tape. One of them is when we have a good idea of what the opposition is about and the techniques he's using - then you can turn around and begin your resistance to all the types of manipulations and so forth. So I think that the... seeing that there were four or five *"theme songs"* - he kept repeating them over and over again.

For example this business which I think is so important... that people fail to distinguish between the ostensible reason and the real reason. In other words, if you want someone to do something and you know that initially he'll be balky at doing that because it's against his morals or against his religious beliefs, you have to substitute another reason that will be acceptable. And then, after he accepts it and it's a fait accompli then there's just no turning back.

D.L.D: Right. It was in that connection that he said, *"People don't ask the right questions."* Too trusting. And this was directed, as I recall, mostly at Americans. I had the feelings he thought Europeans maybe were more skeptical and more sophisticated. That Americans are too trusting and don't ask the right questions.

R.E: With regard to this lack of... almost a lack of discernment. I guess that's basically what he was saying. They were easily tricked or too trusting. The thing that flashed through my mind rather quickly, for example in schools... how quickly so-called AIDS education was introduced.

It did amaze me because if a group stated publicly that they wanted to introduce the concept of sodomy or initiate sex earlier and earlier in children and that was the reason given, most parents I presume wouldn't go for that. So you have to come up with another reason and of course the reason for this so-called AIDS education was to protect children from this disease. But actually, as it turns out, it's really been a great boon for the homosexual network, because through various things like Project Ten they now have access to our children from the youngest years.

These programs are going on from K-12 and I imagine well into college and beyond, so that they are reaching a tremendous segment. Speaking of children, I gather that this speaker... he kept on making the point about, well, old people, they're going to go by the wayside, so I presume that the emphasis for these controllers for this New World Order is really an emphasis on youth.

D.L.D: Absolutely. Yes. Emphasis on youth. This was stated explicitly. People beyond a certain age... they're set in their ways and you're not going to change them. They have values and they're going to stick to them. But you get to the youth when they're young, they're pliable. You mold them in the direction you want them to go. This is correct. They're targeting the young. They figure, *"You old fogies that don't see it our way, you're going to be dying* *off or when the time comes we're going to get rid of you. But it's the youngsters we have to mold in the impression we want."*

Now something on homosexuality I want to expand on, I don't think this came out on the original tape, but there was, first of all, *"We're going to promote homosexuality."* And secondly *"We recognize that it's bizarre abnormal behavior. But, this is another element in the law of the jungle, because people who are stupid enough to go along with this are not fit to inhabit the planet and they'll go by the wayside".*

I'm not stating this precisely the way he said it, but it wasn't too far from there where there was some mention of diseases being created. And when I remember the one statement and remember the other statement, I believe AIDS is a disease which has been created in the laboratory and I think that one purpose it serves is to get rid of people who are so stupid as to go along with our homosexual program. Let them wipe themselves out.

Now it's hard for me make clear how much of it is I'm remembering with great confidence and how much is pure speculation. But as I synthesize this - this is I think what happens... *"If you're dumb enough to be convinced by our promotion of homosexuality you don't deserve a place and you're going to fall by the wayside sooner or later. We'll be rid of you. We'll select out... the people who will survive are those who are also smart enough not to be deluded by our propaganda".* Does that make sense?

R.E: Well, it certainly makes sense for them. And I think also this early sex initiation has the overall purpose which I think we'll get to in depth a little later. But of the sexualization of the population... when he said on the tape, basically, *"Anything goes",* I think that is what we're seeing. It's not so much that, let's say, someone may not adopt the homosexual style for himself, but as a result of the propaganda he certainly will be a lot more tolerant of that type of behavior too.

So it's a desensitization, even for the individual who doesn't go over and accept it for himself.

D.L.D: With the power of propaganda you dare not be against homosexuals, otherwise you get labeled homophobe. You dare not be against any of our programs for women, otherwise you're a male chauvinist pig. It's like anti-Semitism. If this label gets enough currency in the culture that people get shockingly stuck with it. It's easier to keep quiet.

R.E: Another theme was this business about *"CHANGE"*. And I want to get to change in relation to religion and family, but during the period of hearing this tape, I remember going to a MASS and they happened to have at that point DANCING GIRLS FROM THE ALTER. So when I was sitting and getting a chance to listen to the tape I thought, as a Catholic that has been... if you talk about effective change, that has been probably the most difficult and the hardest thing has been to watch our traditional Mass, those things which Catholics have practiced and believed for so long and... at about that time this speech was given which was about late 1969, everything had begun to turn over on its head, so much so that I think many people feel now when they go into a church where there is the Novus Ordo, I think you're almost in a state of constant anxiety because you're not quite sure... What am I going to encounter now?

You look at the little song book; of course that's changed radically and you see, instead of brethren, you see people; or you might see something odd happening up at the alter which is now the *"table"*.

The notion of God as eternal and the teachings of Jesus Christ as eternal, and therefore the teachings of the church as eternal depends on the authority of God, and God brings about change in God's way. What this boils down to me is these people say, *"No, we take the place of God; we establish what will change and what will not change, so if we say that homosexuality or anything is moral today... wasn't yesterday, but it is today. We have said so, and therefore it's moral. We can change tomorrow. We can make it immoral again tomorrow"*. And this is the usurpation of the role of God to define what the peon, the ordinary person's supposed to believe.

D.L.D: So, the idea is, that if everybody is used to change most people aren't going to ask, *"Well who has decided what should be changed and how it should be changed"?* Most people just go along with it, like hemlines, and shoe styles and that sort of thing. So it IS a usurpation of the Rule of God, and if you read the Humanist Manifesto, and somewhere early in the introductory part of it, they say, *"human intellect is the highest good"*. Well, to any human being, what you call the highest good, that's your god. So to these people human intellect being the highest good is god. And where does human intellect reside? Well, in the brain of one or more human beings. So these people, in effect... I don't know think they'd be so candid as to say so, but whether they know it or not what they're saying is, *"I am god. WE are gods, because we decide what is moral what is moral tomorrow, what is going to be moral next year. WE determine change."*

R.E: That's right. And of course, in a nutshell, you've just explained the human potential, the New Age, all the new esoteric movements that we've seen. But with regard to change, he seemed to acknowledge that there were a couple of entities which traditionally blocked this change and therefore made people resistant to constant manipulation.

And of course one of those is the family, and that would include grandmothers, grandfathers, our ethnic background and so forth and I guess I was impressed by everything he seemed to mention whether it was economics, music... had the overall effect of diminishing the family and enhancing the power of the state.

That was a constant theme, and therefore when we're evaluating things I think one of the things we should generally say to ourselves is, "What effect does that have on family life, and the family and I think if every congressman or senator asked that question we probably wouldn't have much action up on Capitol Hill, because almost everything coming down the pike has an effect of disavowing, hurting the family life and enhancing and expanding the power of government.

D.L.D: It has an ostensible purpose, and then it has a REAL purpose.

R.E: Yes, and as a so-called helping professional your ability to say that is very interesting. The other factor is this whole factor of religion, and he was talking basically about a religion without dogma, a religion that would have a little bit from all the other traditional religions so no one would really feel uncomfortable, and he said, rather condescendingly, some people need this and if they need it we'll manufacture something that they need. But of course it can't be anything that would declare any-thing that were moral absolutes or the natural law. Which means that the main target of this group of controllers of course, was and is the Roman Catholic Church and he mentioned the Roman Catholic Church specifically.

D.L.D: Religion's important because it is eternal and we... people who would follow the church will not buy our rules about change. But if we make our own religion, if we define what is religion then we can change it as it suits us. Yes, the Roman Catholic Church... I was kind of flattered sitting here as a catholic, hearing it pointed out that the church is the one obstacle that, he said, *"We have to change that. And once the Roman Catholic Church falls, the rest of Christianity will fall easily".*

R.E: I notice that, as the conversation went on, he said, *"Now you may think Churches will stand in the way, but I want to tell you that they will HELP us"*, and he didn't say they will help us, all except the Roman Catholic Church... he said, *"They will help us"*, and unfortunately...

D.L.D: He was right.

RE: He didn't say this explicitly, but again it was one of those themes that came through... he apparently thought the use of words was real important because he mentioned this with regard to a number of things, like the Bible. The very same as the psychiatrist, Miralu mentioned that *"if you want to control the people, you control the language first"*. Words are weapons. He apparently knew that very well and I think the controllers as a whole know this very well. Of course, it's part of their campaign.

But that little statement about words, that "words will be changed". When I heard that I thought... *"Instead of saying 'alter' you say 'table'. Instead of saying 'sacrifice' you say 'meal' with regard to the Mass"*, and people say, "That's not important". Of course, you know that's VERY important, otherwise, why would they bother to change it? Otherwise, why go through all this rigmarole if it isn't important? It's obviously important for them because they know WITH THE CHANGING OF WORDS YOU CHANGE IDEAS.

D.L.D: They're exerting a lot of effort and time to change it and they're not exerting effort on things that are NOT important, so yes, you're absolutely right. The priest no longer has the role... in some cases he no longer has the role the priest formerly had. Because words carry meaning. There's the dictionary definition, but I think we all know that certain words carry meaning that is a little bit hard to put into words... but they carry meaning.

So yes, controlling the language... you THINK in your language. You think to yourself in English or Spanish or whatever language you're familiar with, but when you think, you talk to yourself and you talk to yourself in words, just the way you talk to other people. And if you can control the language with which one person speaks to himself or one person speaks to another you've gone a long way towards controlling what that person is ABLE - what he is CAPABLE of thinking, and that has both an inclusionary and an exclusionary component to it. You set the tone....

R.E: Take the word GAY, for example. I have some old tapes by Franz Layhar and he talks about the GAY Hussars, you know... the happy soldiers... and now you couldn't quite use that same word, could you? But you know, the word homosexual, sodomite has been replaced with the term *"gay"*, represents an ideology not only a word and when you use it, it's tacit to saying, *"Yes, I accept what your interpretation of this is".*

D.L.D: They probably had a committee working for months to pick which word they were going to use for this. The word *"gay"* carries a connotation, first of all, which is inaccurate. Most homosexuals are not at all gay. They tend to be pretty unhappy people. Despite all the publicity that tells them they can and should feel comfortable with what they're doing, most of them deep down inside don't... (both talking at the same time here).

R.E: I suppose they're going to come up with a sadophobia for those who have a hang-up about sadomasochism and a pedophobia for those who have difficulties with pedophilia, so we can just look forward to this I think. I guess we can look forward to it to the extent we permit ourselves... that we permit the opposition to have access to the brain.

D.L.D: And to dictate the truth WE use. Sex education is NOT education. It's conditioning, and we should never use the term *"sex education"*. It's a misnomer. If they control the vocabulary, then they can control the way we can think and the way we can express ideas among ourselves and to anybody. But *"sex conditioning"*, "sex initiation" is much more accurate and we should insist on that. We should never use terms *"homophobia"* and *"gay"*. Homosexual is homosexual. It's not at all gay.

R.E: That's right. In fact we're probably going to have to do some homework on... probably of all the popular movements in the U.S. Probably the pro-life movement is the most sensitive to words.

Talking about media events and access to the brain, I remember the first speech Bush gave in which he talked about the New World Order... I remember jumping halfway off my seat. That term. Here he is, the president, saying New World Order as if it was something everyone knew about. And someone looking across the room said, *"I heard that. What did he say"? And I said, "He said, 'New World Order'!" And they said, "What does that mean? Why is that extraordinary?"*

So, I think one of the weapons we have against the controllers is that if we can cut off his access to our mind then we have a shot at escaping the manipulation, if not totally - at least escape a portion of the manipulations. Remember, one of the books on Chinese POWs pointed out that some of their survivors in order NOT to be brainwashed broke their eardrums. And in that way - not being able to hear - the enemy could not have access to their brain and therefore they were able to survive where others did not.

And in our popular culture we have a number of things... TV and radio probably primarily, that are the constant means by which the opposition has access to our brain and to our children's brains. So I think the logical conclusion, and one of the common-sense conclusions is that if you don't want the enemy to have access you have to cut off the lines of access... which would be in homes to simply either eliminate altogether, or control by other forms....

D.L.D: Take the networks at their word. They say, *"if you don't like our programming, turn it off"*. And we should. We should say, *"Yeah. You're right."* And we should turn it off. And let the advertisers spend their money on an audience that isn't there.

As a pediatrician I'm always interested in how kids do things and how kids are like adults, and whether you're talking about International politics where one nation goes to war with another or kids on the playground, there are certain things that are common. It's just that kids on the playgrounds do it on a smaller scale. But you mention cutting off access to your brain... somebody says, I don't want to hear it. And I remember hearing kids on a playground... somebody says..."*ya-na-na na naa-na*", and they're teasing the kid... What's he do? He puts his hands over his ears. Says I'm not going to listen. And the kid who's trying to torment him will try to pull his hands away and be sure that he listens. And it's the same....

R.E: Words. Words entering. And the child knows. Words have meaning. They're hurting him.

D.L.D: Goebels knew it. Lenin knew it. CBS knows it. It's interesting; the principle stands - across the board. It just gets more complicated as you get older. More sophisticated. But watch kids on a playground and you'll learn a whole lot about adults.

R.E: Yes. We're all nodding our heads at that one. This Dr. Day was very much into the whole population control establishment, and he was of course in favor of abortion. But as he started talking about the aged and euthanasia I recall one of the population- control books saying that birth control without death control was meaningless.

And one of the advantages in terms… if one was favorable toward the killing of the aged… one of the favorable things is in fact abortion for the simple reason that — universally speaking — abortion has the result of bringing about a rather inordinate chopping off of population at the front end. That is, at the birth end. And the inevitable effect is that you will have a population that is top heavy with a rapidly aging population which is the current state in the United States.

So, inevitably, if you are going to go about killing the young, especially at the pace we seem to have adapted ourselves to in this country, then invariably you're going to have to do something about all those aging populations. Because, the few children who <u>are</u> born, after all, they cannot be expected to carry this tremendous burden of all these people. So you're cutting one end and therefore, inevitably, as you pointed out on the tape, he was saying, "Well, these few young people who are permitted to be born will feel this inevitable burden on them and so they'll be more desensitized."

They'll be more warmed up to the idea of grandma and grandpa having this little party and then shuffle them off to wherever they shuffle off to. And whether it's taking the *"demise"* pill or going to a death camp, or....

D.L.D: There was a movie out sometime back called *"Soylent Green".* Remember that movie? I didn't see the whole movie, but Edward G.

Robinson liked to sit in the theatre and listen to Beethoven's Pastoral Symphony as he was to take his demise pill.

R.E: That's right. He also made the point that the food the people were eating were each other. But as he said, as long as it's done with dignity and humanely... like putting away your horse.

D.L.D: That's a little bit like pornography. Years back kids would come across pornography. It was always poor photography and cheap paper. Then Playboy came out with the glossy pages and really good photography, so then pornography is no longer cheap. It's respectable. We went to a movie at the Pittsburgh Playhouse. I took my son along. It was the Manchurian Candidate. During the previews of the things that are going to come there was a title I don't remember but it was (inaudible) in Technicolor with classical music in the background.

And it was a pornographic movie. And I said, well, if you have a guitar then it's pornography; but if you have classical movie then it converts it into art. It was pornography.

It's an example of what you were saying. As long as it's done with dignity, that's what counts. If you kill someone with dignity, it's ok. If you have pornography with classical music it's art. That was the point I was trying to make.

R.E: Again, talking about the family. Currently I know there are an awful lot of people who are out of jobs and he [Dr. Day] had quite a lot of things to say about, for example, heavy industry. I guess the shock was that this man... I wasn't surprised that he knew a lot about population control, abortion, and at the other end — euthanasia.

But what DID surprise me was that he was an individual who was talking about religion, law, education, sports, entertainment, food... how could one individual have that much input? Now one could say, *"well, it didn't pan out"*. But we know listening to these recollections twenty years later... except perhaps for some minor things, everything that he has said has come to pass and almost beyond imagination. How COULD one individual talk with such authoritative, non-questioning... that this was the way THIS was going to happen and THIS was going to happen in "fashion" and THIS was going to happen on TV and there were going to be video recorders before I ever heard of the word.

D.L.D: I think what happens... certainly one individual hears this, but the plans are by no means made by one or a small number of individuals. Just as industrial corporations which have a board of directors, with people from all sorts of activities who sit on the board of this corporation, and they say, *"Now if we do this to our product, or if we expand in this area what will that do to banking? What will that do to clothing? What will that do... what impact, ripple effect will that have on other things?"* And I'm sure that whoever makes these plans they have representatives from every area you can think of.

So they'll have educators, they'll have clothing manufacturers - designers; architects... across the board. I'm sure they get together and have meetings and plan and everybody puts in his input, just the way a military operation goes. What will the Navy do? Will they bombard the shore? What will the Air Force do? Will they come in with air cover? What will the infantry do? It's the same thing. These people, when they plan, they don't miss a trick.

They have experts in every field and they say, *"Well, if we do this, that and the other.. John, what will that do to your operation?"* And John will be in position to feed back, "Well this is what I think will happen." So it certainly covers a broad range of people. And for one individual to be able to say all of this in the two hours that he spoke to us, really tells us that he was privy to a lot of information.

R.E: That's right. He must have been sitting in on one of those boardrooms at least at some point. And I think not at the highest level from his position, but enough, because anyone in the population control would be associated with names of foundations... powerful foundations, <u>powerful</u> organizations...

D.L.D: And I'm sure there was a lot in the plans that he never heard. He wasn't a four-star general in this outfit. He wouldn't be in on the whole story.

R.E: Well, too bad he couldn't have talked for six hours instead of two, and we might have had a lot more information. There was another aspect that I found fascinating in listening to this. This whole aspect of privacy... he mentioned that as the private homes went by we would have individuals, non-family members perhaps sharing our apartments.

As I understand that is becoming more popular out in California. Could California and New York being the coast states, did he say... That's right... PORT cities that bring in things so that they can eventually work their way to middle America. But this is about privacy. When he was talking, for example, about the area of sex, he made some interesting remarks. One of them that hit me like a ton of bricks was this business about; *"We must be open about sex"*. As if there can't be any fear of the person that does not hesitate to open up to the public. Now, if you look at these so-called sex initiation programs in the schools where the children are forced either through writing or through verbal expression to talk about all aspects of the sexual sphere...

D.L.D: .... of our right to investigate even your sex life. Your money will be easy. We'll have it all on computer. We'll know more about it than you do. But we have to form a generation where the most intimate activity which two people can have is public, or can be public. Therefore, it's harder to have any private thoughts and you can't buck the system if everything you think and do is public knowledge. But the planners won't be that open about their own lives. They'll reserve their privacy. It's for the rest of us.

R.E: Yes. Just like their listening to concerts and operas, but for the mass media they're pumping in hard rock. That was another fascinating thing. For example, the... and I know this has come to pass because I deal with a lot of young people... the young people have their own radio stations for their music and adults have their own and never the twain shall meet. And when they do there's usually a clash. And I think the same is probably true with a lot of the classical movies. I can remember when I was growing up and my dad had the radio on, I think it was a kind of general music. I didn't say, "Dad, I don't like that music; turn to another station". Whereas now there is a fabricated generational gap which puts the family at the disadvantage.

D.L.D: And it creates conflict within the family, which is one of the spin-off benefits to them. If you're constantly fussing at your kids, you don't like the music they're playing, and they're constantly fussing at you because they don't like what you're playing... that does bad things to the bonds of affection that you would like to be nurtured in the family.

R.E: It would appear, that any resistance movement against the population controllers would probably be based on families strengthening themselves in a number of ways. One of them being to make sure that children know about grandma and grandpa and where did they come from and developing a whole... getting out the family albums and making sure that children know they have roots, first of all. And secondly, that their family is stable. One father, one mother, with children, with grandfathers. Those of us who have them should hold on to them.

Toward the end of the tape there was a reference - at the time everything would be coming together - how this New World Order would be introduced to a population which, at this point I think they would assume would be acceptable to it.... how was this put? We're just going to wake up one morning and changes would just be there? What did he say about that?

D.L.D: It was presented in what must be an over-simplified fashion, so with some qualifications, here's the recollections I have... That in the winter, and there was importance to the winter - on a weekend, like on a Friday an announcement would be made that this was or about to be in place... That the New World Order was now the System for the World and we all owe this New World Order our allegiance.

And the reason for winter is that - and this was stated - people are less prone to travel in the winter, particularly if they live in an area where there's ice and snow. In summer it's easier to get up and go. And the reason for the weekend is, people who have questions about this, Saturday and Sunday everything's closed and they would not have an opportunity to raise questions, file a protest and say no.

And just that period over the weekend would allow a desensitizing period so that when Monday came and people had an opportunity maybe to express some reservations about it, or even oppose it... there would have been 48 hours to absorb the idea and get used to it.

R.E: What about those who decided they didn't want to go along?

D.L.D: Somewhere in there it was that... because this is a *"New Authority"* and it represents a change, then, from where your allegiance was presumed to be, people would be called on to publicly acknowledge their allegiance to the new authority. This would mean to sign an agreement or in some public way acknowledge that you accepted this... authority. You accepted its legitimacy and there were two impressions I carried away. If you didn't... and I'm not sure whether the two impressions are necessarily mutually exclusive because this wasn't explored in great detail... one of them was that you would simply have nowhere to go.

If you don't sign up then you can't get any electric impulses in your banking account and you won't have any electric impulses with which to pay your electric, or your mortgage or your food, and when your electric impulses are gone, then you have no means of livelihood.

R.E: Could you get these things from other people, or would that be... in other words, let's say if you had a sympathetic family...

D.L.D: No you could not because the housing authority would keep close tabs on who is inhabiting any domicile. So the housing authority would be sure that everybody living there was authorized to live there.

R.E: Could I get some food?

D.L.D: Your expenditures, through electronic surveillance would be pretty tightly watched so if you were spending too much money at the super market, somebody would pick this up and say, *"How come? What are you doing with all that food? You don't look that fat. You don't have that many people. We know you're not entertaining. What are you doing with all that food?"* And these things then would alert the...

R.E: I have seven people in my basement who object to the New World Order and I'm feeding them and then they said, well, one has to go.

D.L.D: They don't belong there and you can't feed them and since you're sympathetic to them, maybe your allegiance isn't very trustworthy either.

R.E: Yes. We see this... I think the Chinese experience tells us a great deal about certain things. For example, when they wanted to enforce the *"One child family"*... they cut off all education for the second child. Your food rations were cut so you couldn't get the right amount of food, and if they found ways around that, they instituted compulsory abortions and compulsory plugging in of the IUD's.

Somewhere in the tape this business about *"People can carry two conflicting ideas around - or even espouse two conflicting ideas as long as they don't get too close together"*. And what immediately came to mind is... here we have an organization like Planned Parenthood... *"freedom to choose"*, yet they support population control programs which is of course NOT the freedom to choose. And then when they're called into account and someone says, "Now wait a minute here. You're, 'freedom to choose - freedom to choose' here, but you're supporting the Chinese program which is compulsory.

I remember a statement from the late Allen Gootmacher, one of the medical directors of Planned Parenthood and he said, *"Well, if people limit their families and do what we say, fine. But if we need compulsory population control, we're going to have it."*

What would happen with people who wouldn't go along, and particularly that point about, *"There wouldn't be any martyrs"?* That was significant, because I recall having watched some movies about the Third Reich that many times they would come late in the evening and people would be taken from their home, but neighbors would never ask, "Where did they go?" They knew where they went!

D.L.D: Solzhenitsyn mentions that in the Gulag Archipelago.

R.E: I think this is very similar to what we would see. People would just disappear and you would not ask because it might endanger yourself or your family. But you would know where they went. If you ask questions, you draw attention to yourself and then you might follow them to where they went. So you mind your own business and step over the starving man on the street who didn't go along.

D.L.D: He didn't go into detail about precisely how this would come about but it's not too hard to imagine. Yes. In the past, the Nazi's came, the Communists came in the middle of the night, people just disappeared and one simple way to do this is that if you're cut off from all economic support and you have no place to live and nothing to eat... we already see a lot of homeless now.

I just had a man in the office this morning talking about he and his child seeing people living in boxes in downtown Pittsburgh today. When the New World Order is here and you're living in a box, we can't have people littering the place, so you come around in the wagon and you pick them up.

If your frame of mind as you're growing up and formed is that, *"Human value resides in being productive; you have to have a prestigious position or at least perform something useful - make a contribution"*, and the truck comes by to pick up some guy living in a box and he's not making any contribution, who's going to get excited about it? You know... he's sub-human; he's a fetus; he's a zygote; he's a derelict, and fetuses and zygotes and derelicts are all the same animal. So what do you do with them? You dispose of them. Who gets excited about it?

R.E: I recall that when the Chinese Communists came into power one of the first things that they taught in schools was not any thoughts about specific political ideology, but about evolution and that man was just an animal and if man was just an animal then we won't mind being herded and having masters who keep tabs on the animals and we're one big ant colony and we've got someone to direct traffic and...

Speaking of traffic. We talked about the aged and again - people hearing this tape, it's phenomenal how many times these things on this tape will hit you. I just came back from New Jersey which has a lot of retirement-type villages and I've been there over a period of years and there's a structure around a retirement home which has been uncompleted for at least two or three years. Now they've recently completed it. It's kind of a roadway, but I think it would be easier to get out of a complex at a playland it is so complicated. And yet the whole area has elderly people driving.

And we are a fairly middle-aged couple and for the life of me we couldn't figure out how we were going to get out, what we were going to do and so I asked some of the residents... *"Doesn't it bother you that they haven't fixed this road for years and now you can't just go across the street which would have been the logical thing?"* You have to go down and they have a jug-handle and you have to go over and under, so it takes you so long, and the woman replied to me, *"Well you know, we just don't go out. We just don't go out".*

So here we have this little retirement village where they've made it very difficult for a population, maybe several hundred homes in this plat with only one exit and the exit involves such a great deal of bother, they say they just cut down on the number of times they have to go out shopping.

D.L.D: Right away it makes me wonder... if it's difficult to get out, it's also difficult to get in probably for visitors.

R.E: These retirement homes sort of remind me of an elephant burial ground. The one thing you notice is that there are no children. There's not the laughter of children in these homes.

D.L.D: My experience has been, these people in the retirement homes, when they see a child they just blossom. They're really delighted to see a child. Sure they're happy to have their sons and daughters come and other adults, but when they see a child - and it doesn't have to be their own - it has a very beneficial effect on their mood. And if these older people aren't seeing children, the other side of that coin is, the children aren't seeing older people either. So if you don't get used to seeing older people, they don't exist.

R.E: And that's why, with the family, making sure your children see their grandparents very often, no matter how much that entails, the trouble with the logistics, etc... it's certainly worthwhile because, again if you never see someone and you don't learn to love them and you never have any contact with them, when someone says, *"Well it's time for your grandpa to check out"*, it's like, *"Who's that?"*

Who's going to defend and fight for someone they never even saw before? Oh, I remember one of the phrases. So many of these things... you only have to hear them once and they stick in your mind. It's so jarring.

We've already discussed *"sex without reproduction"*, then you also said the technology would be there for "reproduction without sex" and this is a whole other area because it's contradictory. If a land is so overpopulated, then you would want to diminish sexual activity, get rid of pornography, get rid of everything that was sexually stimulating. But, no. It's a contrary. You want to Increase sexual activity but only insofar as it doesn't lead to reproduction. That was the message, right?

D.L.D: Yes, and this is my own extension. He didn't say this, but that leads to slavery because if you become enslaved to your gratification, whether it's sex, food or whatever, then you're more easily controlled, which is one of the reasons the celibate priesthood is so important. And so many priests don't even understand that. But if you're addicted to sex... if sex is divorced from reproduction, something you do for gratification only - I won't try to parallel that with food because you can't go without food - then you can be more easily controlled by the availability or the removal of the availability of sex.

So that can become an enslaving feature. Now, reproduction without sex... what you would get then would have all the desirable attributes of a human being without any claim to human rights. The way we do it now, we say, you're human because you have a father and mother... you have a family and so you're a human being with human rights. But if your father was a petrie dish and you mother was a test tube, how can you lay claim to human rights? You owe your existence to the laboratory which conveys to you no human rights.

And there is no God, so you can't go for any God-given human rights, so you're an ideal slave. You have all the attributes of a human being but you don't have any claim on rights.

R.E: In *"Brave New World"* they had the caste system, the alphas, the omegas, etc. The way they brought about the different caste systems was that in the decanting, or birthing rooms, the individual who was to do menial or slave labor... work in the mines... received just a little bit of oxygen to the brain so they learned to love their slavery and they were very happy.

They didn't know any better. They didn't have the wherewithal to do things, but the higher in the caste you got, the more oxygen you got to your brain. So we actually had a group of sub-human beings who loved their slavery. In the past slaves probably didn't love their slavery very much, but in this case, we have this technology which will make people love their slavery, and each caste loved being what they were in *"Brave New World"*. And any of our listeners who hasn't read that recently...

D.L.D: You may remember the slogan that was above the Nazi concentration camps... something about, *"Work is Peace and Work is Happiness"*. I don't remember if it was Buchenwald or Auschwitz. My recollection of words isn't precise, but the idea is what counts. And here's Huxley, writing Brave New World, saying basically the same thing before Hitler was even in power, so Huxley knew something.

R.E: He came from a family that probably contributed at least in part to this New World Order. A number of the English authors... H.G. Wells... from that period and from those associations who highlighted the concepts of what was coming down the path.

I can remember reading Brave New World in high school, and thought, *"Boy, is this fantasy land"*. Thirty years later and I said, *"This is scary"*. There seems to be kind of a similarity between his writings and the talk given by Dr. Day, because you get kind of a mixed message in Brave New World, that these things are not really good. It would be better if man still had a sense of humor, a sense of privacy, if the family still existed.. but, it's inevitable. They're going to go. Too bad. I feel a little sorry about that. A little sentiment, but the New Order has to come in and we have to make room for it.

And I got that same impression from the things that were said about this Day tape. He wasn't real happy about some of the things, but they're going to occur anyway, so make it easier on yourself. The more you accept it the easier it's going to be when it comes around, and I'm kind of doing you a favor - you physicians out there this evening - I'm going to make it easier for you by telling you in advance what's coming and you can make your own adjustments.

D.L.D: Somewhere in Scripture… I think it was after the flood, God said, *"I will write my law on man's hearts"*, and I feel the same parallel that you do between Dr. Day's reaction to what he was exposed to and mine… seeming not totally accepting of this. Huxley seeming not totally accepting of what he wrote about but both saying, "Well, there's a certain inevitability to all of this, so let's try to talk about the best parts of it. It's going to be good for people. Technology will be better, quality of life will be better… so you live a few years shorter."

But they both do seem to send out messages not buying the whole package…

R.E: And maybe wishing some people would ask more questions. Looking back over history there are many individuals who had an idea of what a New World Order should be, certainly Hitler and Stalin did, but what was lacking during these periods is that they lacked the technology to carry many a many of the things out… surveillance, constant monitoring… but in this so-called New World Order it's going to be very difficult to escape because technology will provide those means which had been lacking those totalitarian individuals from years ago.

D.L.D: I can't remember on the original tapes, did I mention the phrase where he said, *"This time we're going to do it right!"* ?

R.E: No. You didn't.

D.L.D: There were so many details to remember. But when he mentioned bringing in the New World Order, he said, ***"This time we're going to do it right"***.

And right away, I'm wondering, *"what do you mean, 'this time'?"*. There was no explicit explanation of that, but I think it's fairly easy to infer that previous efforts had to do with the Third Reich... Your point about the technology is critical with computers and all means of exchange being controlled by electronic impulse.

Nobody has any wealth. You own nothing of value except access to electronic impulses which are beyond your control. A cashless society. So when your reward for working is [nothing more than] impulses on the computer and the only claim you have is these impulses and the people who run the system can give or take them as they choose. Up until this time there was no way the statement in the Book of Revelation that said, *"No man can buy or sell unless he has the mark of the beast"*... there's no way that could have been enforced.

People could say I'll trade you a bushel of tomatoes for a bushel of wheat. If you'll drive my kids to school I'll give you six ears of corn. Bartering. And even not going necessarily that primitive, there was always gold and silver and other forms of money that were even better than bartering. But with this cashless society, I believe this is the first time in the history of the human race where the entire population of the world can be controlled economically so that somebody can say, *"I pushed the right buttons and I know how much credit you have electronically; I know where you spend your money electronically; and you cannot buy, you cannot sell unless you get on my computer."*

Right now you have a half a dozen credit cards in your pocket, but pretty soon it will be narrowed to one credit card and then when we... you know the ostensible reason is that when people lose their credit cards and we have to get rid of that and put the implant in... where it has to be accessible to the scanner... in your right hand or in your forehead.

R.E: Speaking of scanner. When we had the TV War..... the Gulf War? It was the first war where you just sit there and 24 hours a day just like being on the battlefield there. There were several points made about the advances in technology and how they could spot just one little individual down in... they used the constant reference to pinpoint... *"pinpoint"*. I imagine with the different technologies they can also pinpoint a couple of renegades in the New World Order. The technology which was applicable to a so- called 'enemy' can also be applicable to this controlling the order.

D.R.D: Exactly. It's infra-red stuff that's... I'm sort of amateurish about this, but any heat source like a deer, a human being, a renegade... can be picked up by an infra-red scanner and you get sort of an outline of whether it's a deer or sheep or whatever.

My first hearing about them was in the Vietnam War where our troops used them to detect the enemy. That's twenty-some years ago, so they're probably even more sophisticated now than they were then; but with this kind of surveillance it would be pretty hard for anybody to escape and say,

"Well, I'm just going to go out into the mountains and be a hermit and escape the New World Order. I can shoot deer and eat berries and survive and I've got a wife who's pretty sturdy and she'll be able to survive and we'll do what the Indians did before Columbus got here and we'll all survive". The New World Order will say, "No you won't because we're gonna find you".

R.E: Even in Brave New World they had a group of people who still lived as a family and the women breast-fed and they were called savages. But we won't have any savages. We're cultured, we'll be thin and our teeth will be straight.

D.L.D: Something also that was mentioned; forests could — and if necessary <u>would</u> — be leveled or burned. Now this comes out of this movement... goddess mother earth, and how we have to protect the environment... but if we want to get someone who's trying to get away we'll burn down the whole forest. We'll find them. That was stated. Deforestation could be and would be brought about to make sure that nobody gets outside the control of the system.

R.E: We're drawing to a close here. How did you feel after... well, it's been about 22 years now since that original lecture and there probably isn't a day that goes by - at least since I've heard the tape - that I don't think about the things that this Dr. Day said.

D.L.D: You get constant reminders. Not a day goes by something doesn't say, *"That reminds me of..."* such and such, whether it's surveillance or security...

R.E: ... or clothing. I opened up a toy catalogue the other day and noticed there didn't happen to be any baby dolls in this toy catalogue... of course going back to the idea that we don't want little girls to by thinking about babies. They only had one little doll and it was kind of an adult doll. And nothing that would raise anyone's maternal instincts. Well, Doc, what's the prognosis?

D.L.D: Left to man alone I think the technology is already here and with technological progress, I think it is inevitable -- if man is left to his own devices -- that some men will be able to assert total control over other men... other people. Man left to his own devices... the tendency is -- in groups like this, then -- is for internal dissension to arise where the leaders would be at each other's throats too... each saying, *"No, I'm more powerful than you. I deserve more than you"*.

R.E: Who will control the controllers?

D.L.D: Yeah. They would stab themselves. I think so. They would create their own seeds of destruction while they're creating the system. But the other thing I wonder if indeed this may be time for our Lord to come back and say, *"Enough's enough. Because you're going to destroy my planet earth. I am in charge of the planet. I'm in charge of mankind. Mankind will be destroyed if I say. I will not allow my creatures to assume and exert this degree of control where you're going to destroy the whole thing."*

R.E: What I was just thinking as you were just saying that is that in the past, dictators could kill people, they could torture them, but essentially they could not change what it meant to be a human being. They could not change human nature. Now we are going to have with this new Genome Project, a multi-billion dollar project where they're going to be getting a tab on everyone's genes. No one shall escape. Everyone shall have their genetic codes and with this opens the door to manipulation to change the very meaning of what it MEANS to be human.

And if one has an entity then that no longer has free will, you just have to wonder if that point out Lord says, *"Enough".*

D.L.D: Just as Lucifer set himself up as God in the beginning, some people now would set themselves up as God and say, *"I control the computers, I control the genomes, I control everything, I am God..."* and at that point He would have to say, *"No, you are not!* I have to demonstrate to you... you're NOT. I'm still God. You're just a creature"

RE: And as you said on the original tape, we believe in what our Lord has said, in that He will not leave us orphans. He will be with us 'til the end of time.

D.L.D: This right away now begs the questions, when they come around and say, *"It's your turn to sign the allegiance form"*... what are you going to do? When Henry the eighth came around and said, either sign here and join... and while he was saying it they were throwing the noose over the limb of the oak tree, and slipping the noose around your neck and saying, *"you want to sign this or do we slap the horse out from under you?"* and a lot of people said I won't sign it and they were martyred.

Despite his having said there will be no martyrs, certainly there will be martyrs. The implication of his statements were that they would not be recognized as martyrs, but there will be martyrs and they will be RECOGNIZED as martyrs. Maybe not the same way as in the past but I think this is something people should sort of prepare themselves for.

When I'm nose to nose with this choice, *"ether sign this allegiance or we're going to put you in a boxcar and you're going out to Arizona, to the desert..."* I think we have to be prepared to make a decision.

R.E: I think it would be an understatement to say that this tape has great meaning and it's like a forewarning and it gives us ideas of things we should do and things we shouldn't do and I think everybody listening to the tapes will come up with things he can do on a small scale. I think that's the beauty of this thing. As he was talking... it wasn't real earth shattering things he was talking about. He was talking about little things. Television. Things that we do every day. Things that are under our control. The books we read.

And I think some of these changes if they are going to occur will occur with the individual person within that family, with him getting the word out and then doing the little things. I think they matter over the long haul, the most.

D.L.D: Just as with the prisoners who survived the brainwashing, I think people who are Spiritually oriented, who are thinking about God, thinking about their relationship WITH God, are the ones who will then be better prepared or equipped to survive this world and the next. Whereas, those who are just focused on meeting their needs right now, strictly the material needs of the day, they're more easily controlled.

Under the threat of losing your comforts or losing your food or losing your head or whatever, certainly some people are going to yield, and those who I think will survive and I really mean both in this life and the next - they're going to have to be the ones who are prepared because it's my belief when the time comes to make the decision... *"Are you going to sign on or not?"*... it's too late to begin preparation and start saying, *"Well, let me think about this."*

You won't have time to think about it. You're either going to say yes or no. I hope a lot of us make the right decision.

R.E: I do so too, and I think the tape will change as many lives and have hopefully as good an effect as it had on mine and on yours and so let me thank you very much.

Source/Reference: U.S. Coalition for Life; Box 315, Export, Penn 15632

About the Author

D r. Vic Naumov, D.C., is the Founder and Director of the Naumov Chiropractic and Performance Nutrition Center, located in New Milford, N.J.

After almost 20 years in private practice, Dr. Vic Naumov has discovered that health is an "expression" of the body's ability to adapt to physical, chemical and mental stimuli accordingly. This led him to coin the term *"The Adaptability Factor."* Along the way, he learned that deficiencies and toxicities are the two primary factors in the cause of mostly all diseases. Today, as a noted organic healthcare practitioner, independent researcher and consultant, Dr. Vic focuses on teaching his clients how they can "Nurture Nature" and adapt to their highest potential.

Dr. Vic is a graduate of Montclair State University, where he earned a Bachelor's Degree prior to graduating from New York Chiropractic College. He is also a life-long, multi-sport athlete who lives an active, healthy lifestyle along with his family.

Made in the USA
Middletown, DE
16 August 2017